PHYSICS OF THE EARTH

THE WORLD OF SCIENCE LIBRARY

ADVISORY EDITOR: ROBIN CLARKE
EDITOR OF SCIENCE JOURNAL

PHYSICS OF THE EARTH

T. F. Gaskell

551
Ga

FUNK AND WAGNALLS   NEW YORK

17,611

CONTENTS

INTRODUCTION

Early philosophers satisfied their interests by studying the land that they could see around them. Later they were backed by enterprising explorers who ventured across the oceans to find new continents. Today the whole surface of the earth is accurately mapped, and aerial photography is filling in the fine detail; Everest has been scaled, the Arctic ice cap traversed, and the last island discovered. Many scientists and explorers are now satisfying their curiosity and their adventurous urges by going, instead, out into space and down into the deep oceans. Already the moon has been conquered, and the challenge of the deepest ocean trench overcome. As a result, we are learning a great deal more about the workings of our planet and about its place in the solar system and among the stars. It is therefore a good time to take stock of our knowledge of the earth, the better to appreciate the significance of the new experimental discoveries that are currently being made.

If we look back in history we find that our understanding of the earth has advanced in a series of comparatively few steps. Greek astronomers were the first to substitute a globe for the original flat earth concept—although the existence of a Flat Earth Society still demonstrates the individual attitude of some stalwart seekers after knowledge. Seventeenth-century study of the planetary system led to the determination of the earth's mass. Twentieth-century geophysicists, probing the inside of the earth with waves sent out by earthquakes, have revealed a dense liquid core wrapped round by a thick rock mantle, the whole encased in a thin skin of crustal rocks of the kind that can be seen at the surface.

In the nineteenth century students of geology began to discern order in the wide variety of rock types forming the land features of the earth, and thought was first given to the time it would have taken for an originally molten sphere to cool. Mining experience demonstrated clearly that the earth's interior was hotter than at the surface, and the discovery of radioactivity as a source of internal heating has subsequently made the study of the earth's heat balance an important factor in deducing the planet's structure and geological history.

The need to lay telegraph cables across the ocean first opened the way to the study of the sea bed, which has since yielded some of the greatest advances in geological knowledge this century. Experiments at sea are expensive, and oceanographical research has been assisted by the navies of the world, which now wish to patrol the seas unseen, instead of travelling in two dimensions, as in the past. Economic rewards, too, have accrued from these marine geology studies: oil and gas have been found in abundance beneath the shallow seas fringing the continents.

The origin of the earth is still in doubt. In general, views have shifted from the idea of a condensation of hot gas to the idea of an accretion of cold particles. The early heating of a cold earth by radioactivity or by gravitational forces could, however, allow a molten sphere at an early stage, as geological observations seem to demand.

In deducing what happened thousands of millions of years ago we are often faced with several plausible explanations, and provided each allows us to arrive at known end points, all must tentatively be accepted as possibilities. In science we often go full circle in our ideas and, whether we believe in continental drift, require Mars to

▶.

have come out of the Pacific, or subscribe to continual manufacture of the sea floor, we should endeavour not to be dogmatic. The theory of continental drift, which was summarily rejected by geophysicists fifty years ago on the grounds that it was impossible, is now generally accepted. It makes a great deal of sense of the world-wide geophysical picture. For example, continents are continually being eroded, and the spoil redeposited in shallow water to form fresh layers of rock. Similar deposits on continents which are now widely separated suggest that these land masses were once joined together.

The mechanism by which continents can drift about the earth, sometimes finding themselves on the equator, and scores of millions of years later moving into polar climates, is probably associated with the plastic flow of rocks softened by radioactive elements below the crustal layer. This would produce splitting and wrinkling of the crustal rocks, accounting for mountain-building, volcanoes and earthquakes, and movement of the continents. A continual movement of the ocean floor is apparently taking place, spreading outwards on both sides of central lines of activity, and carrying the continents away from each other. One day a sample of mantle rock will be brought up by drilling through the earth's crust, and this

The earth in space. 1: the earth photographed by a weather satellite from an altitude of 22,300 miles above the mouth of the river Amazon. The bulge of Africa can be seen on the right. 2: the sun— undistinguished star and hub of our solar system. The arrowed dot represents the disc of the earth on the same scale. 3: a hundred-thousand suns—a detail of the Milky Way and a minute fraction of the total stellar complement of our galaxy. 4: NGC 4594, the 'Sombrero Hat' galaxy (seen edge on), thought to bear a close resemblance to our own galaxy. It comprises some 100,000-million stars and has a diameter of 100,000 light-years. 5: part of a cluster of galaxies about 120-million light-years away. More than 50-million-million galaxies are known, none containing fewer than a million stars

will enable the rate of heat generation to be calculated more exactly, and will also allow the plasticity of mantle rocks at their ambient high temperatures and pressures to be determined. These measurements will help to clarify theories based at present only on surface observations.

The core of the earth is known, from earthquake studies, to be of high density and to be mainly liquid. It is also a good conductor of electricity and is the source of the earth's magnetic field. The earth's magnetism has been a great boon to geophysicists. Just as the old navigators found their way to new lands with the help of the magnetic compass, so today we can plot the movements of the continents themselves by means of fossilized magnetic fields imprinted in the rocks.

Our new knowledge of the earth is rapidly enlarging our capacity to change the world we live in. Today's civil engineers, equipped with nuclear explosives, could melt ice caps and move mountains. It is therefore important that we should learn the fine details of the ways in which nature operates before doing something to upset natural balances that have taken many millions of years to become established. The atomic bomb has brought many problems to the world, but its existence has in one way helped to solve them. The setting up of listening posts to detect underground nuclear test explosions has given a great boost to the seismic technique of probing into the earth, and to the discovery of the detailed processes that occur during earthquakes. It is a pity that large sums of money for increasing our knowledge of natural phenomena are only available under the threat of war, but such spending is needed now if the human race is to avoid catastrophe in the future.

Several trigger mechanisms are now becoming

apparent by which the massive forces of nature could be deliberately or inadvertently turned against us. The great volcanic explosion of 1883 at Krakatoa could be matched by an underwater explosion producing a wave capable of inundating long stretches of coastline; large meteorites might one day be steered on to enemy territory by nuclear charges; holes made in the atmosphere could allow killing ultra-violet rays to shine on selected targets; the climate might be warmed up to melt polar ice caps and drown many of the worlds largest cities by raising the mean sea level. Alternatively, an ice age could be started to freeze up all the temperate zones of the world; or, again, attempts to cause drought in a neighbour's country could be disguised as rain-making experiments. The energy available in the atmosphere, in the earth's rotation and in the sun's rays is enormous, and the more we learn about how it is controlled the greater will become our potential to create and destroy.

The search for nature's secret skills calls for international effort, and working together has already produced friendly co-operation between those who study the earth sciences in different countries. I should like to think that one day we shall achieve world unity in combating natural forces instead of one another.

T. F. G.
London, 1969

THE EARTH'S ORIGIN

The beginning of the earth will always be shrouded in mystery. No one was present to report how it all happened nearly 5,000-million years ago, and it is unlikely that a similar occurrence will ever be witnessed by man. Moreover, the operation was far too vast to be simulated in a modern experiment, even on a model scale. In order to make a reasonable conjecture about the origin of the earth we must rely on deductions from the world that we can see today, and extrapolate backwards using known laws governing the behaviour of matter.

The earth can hardly be called a typical member of the universe. The sun, the stars and the great nebulae are all composed mainly of hydrogen and helium, whereas these elements are almost absent from the atmosphere of the earth. The earth differs even from the outer, larger planets, such as Jupiter and Neptune, which have in common with the stars the fact that they are largely gaseous in composition. The earth's atmosphere is unusual in containing a high proportion of oxygen, which in its turn makes life on earth possible, and the earth itself an even more anomalous object.

Opposite: the earth as seen by the Apollo-8 astronauts on 24 December 1968 during the first manned circumnavigation of the moon. Below: the earth as visualized by Babylonian cartographers c. 4,000 BC

Condensation or accretion?

The eighteenth-century philosopher Kant proposed that a swirling nebula of hot gas originally gave rise to the sun and the planets by a series of local condensations of matter. In 1796 the astronomer and mathematician Laplace modified this concept by proposing condensation to form the sun, which then, owing to the centrifugal effect of its rotation, ejected the planets, the outer planets being thrown off first. These theories are difficult to reconcile with the comparatively slow rotation of the sun. For most of the rotational energy of the solar system resides with the planets, although the sun is nearly a thousand times as massive as all the planets put together. Perhaps this rotational problem can be overcome by postulating the action of a second body. Another star could pass close by the sun and wrench away a string of droplets which would then condense to form the planets. But it is probable that any such droplets which remained within the sun's gravitational field would eventually fall back into the parent body. Only if the sun originally had a

1: the formation of the solar system as proposed by Kant and Laplace. An enormous rotating nebula, or cloud, of gas, as it contracts and increases in temperature to form the sun throws off successive gaseous rings, which cool and condense to form the planets. 2: an alternative theory, proposed by Sir James Jeans in 1901. The gravitational force of a star in near collision with the sun detaches a vast filament of solar material, which, again, gives rise to the planets

companion star that was removed by the near miss of a third star would it be possible to account for the orbital paths of these droplets.

Present–day ideas favour an initially cold planet rather than condensation from a hot gas to a molten liquid which subsequently solidified. Dense 'dust clouds' or 'globules' can be seen in the night sky partially obscuring the stars. Some of these clouds are comparatively near by, between 10,000 and 100,000 times as distant as the sun, and may possibly have resulted from the break-up of a companion star to the sun; from a collision of this companion star with a third, resulting in finely vaporized material; or merely from the capture of a stray cloud by the sun. Such gaseous material would have cooled and its less volatile components have condensed to give a mixture of liquid droplets and solid particles immersed in gas.

This mixture probably rotated in the form of a vast disc with the sun at its centre, and stretched out as far as the present paths of Neptune and

Today there is no generally accepted theory of planet formation. On the one hand, Fred Hoyle and Hannes Alfvén, returning in principle to Kant and Laplace, see a rapidly rotating sun throwing off planetary rings and slowing down as its angular momentum is transferred along the lines of force of its magnetic field to the condensing planets. On the other hand, it is widely argued that the planets were formed out of cold cosmic dust by a process of accretion. The structure of the solar system is accounted for by a series of turbulences in a dust cloud captured and patterned by the sun. Above: a turbulence pattern on lines proposed by Carl Weizäcker. Above left: a gaseous nebula in the constellation Sagittarius. Each arrow indicates a vast opaque dust cloud which may be contracting to form a future star

Pluto. At first, particles would stick together only when they collided, but later, where sufficiently large aggregations had formed, gravitational attraction would cause more material to augment the growing body. As its mass increased, a planet would eventually attract a wide swathe of particles, and would starve its smaller competitors. Some of the asteroids, which are bodies up to a few hundred miles in diameter, may represent incipient planets, stunted in their youth because their larger neighbours snatched the raw material of growth before they could assimilate it.

This 'cold-accretion' process was proposed in order to explain the abundance on the earth of light elements. For if a hot condensation of gas had taken place not only would the earth have lost its hydrogen and helium, but also much of other light elements. If, then, the planets originated as a cold cloud of dust and gas, we must assume that all the bodies orbiting the sun have, or had initially, the same composition, and that this composition was uniform right through the body, since each planetary body was formed by gradual accumulation of the same kind of dust particles. Consistent with this theory is the fact that the stony meteorites which fall to the earth from outer space have a chemical composition similar to that of average terrestrial rocks.

The molten planet

The earth consists of three main layers: a thin crust of rocks like those visible at the surface; a mantle, which stretches halfway to the centre of the earth; and a liquid core. It is possible that the liquid core has formed gradually from the initially cold, solid planet owing to the heat produced by the decay of radioactive uranium, potassium and thorium atoms during the many millions of years

The earth's interior: seventeenth- and twentieth-century models. Opposite top: the system of volcanic chambers and ducts pictured by Athanasius Kircher in his Mundus Subterraneus *(1665). Bottom: the system of concentric spheres which enables modern science to account for the characteristic paths described by earthquake shock waves*

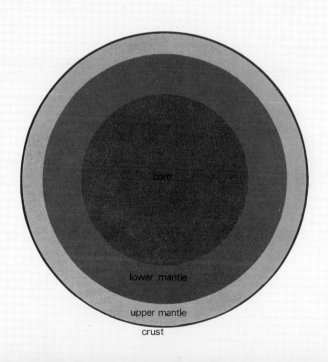

Pouring off the slag. When metallic ores are smelted, non-metallic impurities separate from the pure molten metal and float to the surface. The earth's crust probably formed in a similar way during a molten phase in the planet's history

since the earth's formation. The core could still be increasing in size through the melting and separating out of heavy from lighter elements; and such a gradual growth could explain some of the changes that have occurred during the earth's history. However, geologists have generally preferred an initially molten earth, since it is then easy to explain the earth's crust as a light 'scum' floating atop a molten mass like slag in a blast furnace. Because a molten start to the earth provides a ready explanation for other past occurrences, and because a perfectly valid account of a mechanism for melting the earth after the cold accretion of the solid dust particles is available, the probable course of the earth's history will include a molten state about 4,500-million years ago.

The slow heating of the earth by radioactive uranium, potassium and thorium could not alone explain a totally molten stage since its formation. However, there are other radioactive materials, such as the aluminium isotope Al^{26}, which decay rapidly, so that more than half the atoms would have given out their energy in less than a million years. It is conceivable that the original dust cloud contained sufficient Al^{26} to cause a rapid heating of the planets once they had captured enough Al^{26} and an insulating blanket to contain the heat. The planetary bodies, then, during the first few million years of their life, would therefore gradually become incandescent, and develop from that point as if from a hot-condensation method of origin. No trace would be left of the Al^{26} atoms after 4,500-million years, since they would long since have decayed to a common isotope of magnesium, which has no label indicating its ancestry.

An argument in favour of an early molten stage in planetary life is provided by the examination of iron meteorites. These bodies probably derive from the break-up of small asteroids having iron-alloy cores not unlike that of the earth. A great deal is known about the alloys of iron because of their importance in steel-making; and in particular the temperature conditions under which various crystalline forms of alloys can exist are well documented. The meteoritic iron must have warmed up comparatively quickly, and this would have been impossible in geological time if only uranium, potassium and thorium had been available to provide the initial melting which allowed the formation of iron cores in asteroids. Some rapid heating process is indicated, and again it could have been Al^{26} or some other fast-acting radioactive material.

The moon's significance

The melting of the earth allowed the lighter rocks to float to the surface and solidify as a 20-mile-thick skin of density about 2·8 (times that of pure water). These lighter rocks formed the raw material of the geological cycles of erosion and deposition that have subsequently been instrumental in concentrating minerals. Remarkable, however, is the fact that the 20-mile-thick crust occupies less than a third of the earth's surface and is associated only with the continental land masses. Under the oceans the crust is much thinner—barely 3 miles thick—and is not subject to most continental geological changes.

Alternatively, it is possible to visualize the formation of crustal rocks without needing to postulate a molten earth. As we shall see later, a continual movement of the ocean-floor could take place, and the sea-bed sediments be swept beneath the continents. This process could have produced the continents themselves, with the help

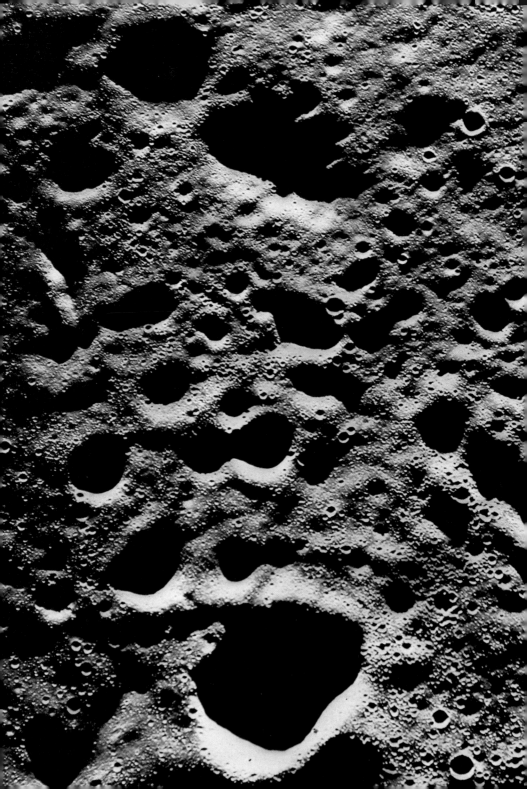

of material brought to the surface by volcanoes and subsequently eroded and deposited as sediment. On this theory the continents are continually growing in size. But there is probably a balance of evidence in favour of the crustal rocks being separated from the primeval planet-building material by melting, and there is a ready explanation of the fact that the continental crust covers only one-third of the earth's surface instead of, as might be expected of a cooling crust, covering the whole surface uniformly.

This explanation concerns the origin of the moon, a subject about which many theories have been woven, and which has produced a great many rather one-sided arguments during the past

The key to a better understanding of the earth's early history may lie on the moon, for there is reason to suppose that both bodies may have shared a similar—perhaps common—origin, and it is possible that evidence long since obliterated on earth by the action of the atmosphere has been preserved on the moon. Opposite and below: moonscapes—apparently peppered and pockmarked by untold millions of meteoritic impacts—as seen by the Apollo-8 *astronauts*

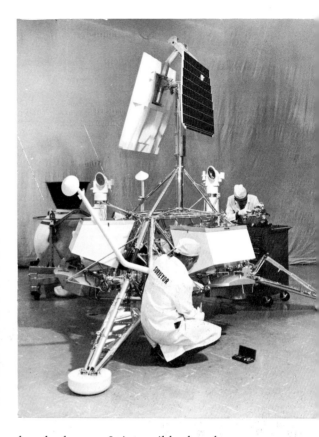

A Surveyor *spacecraft, one of a series designed to soft-land on the moon and test its surface. In 1967 experiments carried out by* Surveyor III *suggested that the moon's surface has a consistency resembling that of a granular terrestrial soil, and* Surveyor V *that it has a composition not unlike that of the earth's surface. The moon sample recovered by the* Apollo-11 *astronauts is, however, unlike earth rock in composition*

hundred years. It is possible that the moon was a small planet which approached the earth and was captured to spend its days orbiting its new parent. On the other hand, the moon may have been a local condensation of gaseous matter surrounding the earth, which solidified to become a satellite. Samples of the moon's surface recovered by astronauts during the Apollo series of expeditions are already yielding facts which could weigh in favour of one theory against another. However, an increasing body of well-informed opinion is swinging towards an old nineteenth-century idea of Darwin's, that the moon is a cast-off fragment of the earth itself.

The earth's core is of a heavy material, probably iron together with a few lighter elements. It is not difficult to imagine the heavy iron alloys settling, under gravitational attraction, towards the centre of a molten earth at the same time that the lighter rocks were solidifying at the surface. At that time in its history the earth was rotating with a much shorter day–about four hours–and the movement of heavy material to the centre caused it to spin even faster. This high-speed rotation of a liquid body, with only a thin containing skin, probably had the effect of changing the spherical shape to a flattened, almost disc-like body; and just as mud is thrown off a rotating cart-wheel, so bits of the earth would have been flung off into space.

However, it can be proved conclusively that only two courses are possible for things that are ejected from the earth, for the theoretical reasoning has been demonstrated by the behaviour of orbiting satellites in recent years. Either the bodies that are hurled skyward continue in their course away from the earth until captured by the sun's gravitational field to become new planets, or they eventually fall back to the earth. In order to put a body, such as the moon, into a satellite path around the earth an *extra* sideways kick, in addition to the upward thrust, is needed. This is why the old idea that the moon was once part of the earth fell into disfavour.

Many good theories have been temporarily discarded because of pontifical statements by respected mathematicians. In the last century, for example, a wealth of practical geological experience in favour of an age for the earth amounting to hundreds of millions of years was brushed aside by Lord Kelvin, who calculated, on the basis of the rate of loss of heat from the earth, that a mere

Neil Armstrong, alighting in the Sea of Tranquillity, becomes the first man to set foot on the moon – at 03.56 GMT, 21 July 1969. His first comments on the surface: 'It's like fine, sandy particles. There seems to be no difficulty in walking around.'

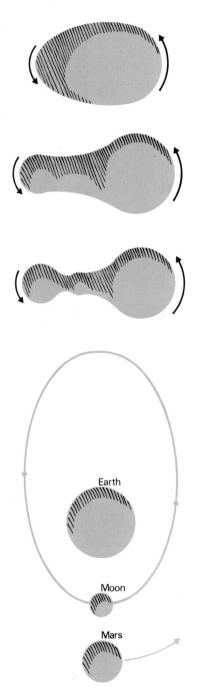

ten-million years would be the maximum span allowable before the earth cooled completely. A few years later Lord Kelvin's assertions were upset by the discovery of radioactivity as a source of heat inside the earth. Then again, the German geologist Alfred Wegener never received credit in his lifetime for his theory of continental drift, because theoretical geophysicists maintained that it was impossible to thrust a solid continent through an equally solid earth's crust. Today, few people dispute the drifting continent hypothesis.

The stumbling block in the theory that the moon was once part of the earth is the need to conceive of *two* bodies leaving the earth together, the second supplying the needed additional kick. If we suppose that the moon and Mars were spun off a rapidly rotating molten earth, and that Mars escaped from the earth's gravitational field to be captured by the sun, the moon—a mere eightieth of the mass of the earth—could accountably be left behind as an earth satellite. And indeed, since the mass of Mars is only one-tenth that of the earth, it is physically possible for it, too, formerly to have been a part of the earth. Moreover, since the density of Mars—about 4—is substantially lower than the earth's density of 5·5, those who assert that Mars is a fundamental planet cannot at the same time uphold the common dust-cloud origin of all planetary matter. If, however, Mars was thrown off a rapidly rotating earth, its density would be expected to be that of the mantle mixed with a little lighter crustal material, for the movement of heavy material to form the earth's core would already have occurred.

Proponents of this theory argue further that Mars and the moon left behind a permanent scar on the earth's surface. Two-thirds of the recently solidified crust was torn away to leave an unsymmetrical but rather more interesting world, with one-third of the surface in the form of land surrounded by a vast ocean. At first the solid continental skin that remained after the exodus of Mars formed a single land mass, and it was only later, as we shall see in the next chapter, that the continents reached their present dispositions. The earth-origin of Mars and the moon, then, not only provides a good reason for the abnormally low densities of these celestial bodies, but also answers the vexing question of why the earth's crust is not evenly distributed all over the earth, with a uniform covering of sea – which is what one would expect in the case of a system which is rotating steadily. The density of the

How the earth-moon system originated is extremely uncertain: of the various hypotheses so far put forward the most plausible seem to be: (1) that the moon was a small planet captured by the earth with the aid of the sun's gravitation; and (2) that the earth and moon were formed together with the planet Mars as the result of the break-up of a single primitive planet. The latter hypothesis (illustrated opposite) is that favoured by the author. Below: The Martian surface from 6,000 miles

moon, 3·4, is readily explained if the moon material is partly earth's mantle and partly crust.

Once the moon was established in orbit around the earth, it began to part company with its parent body. The gravitational pull of the moon on the earth produces tidal fluctuations, but in doing so energy is expended as, for example, when the waters rush through narrow inlets such as the English Channel or the Bering Straits. This loss of energy causes the earth to slow down, so that it now rotates once in 24 hours instead of the few hours when Mars and the moon were thrown off. The effect on the moon of this energy dissipation is to make it gradually recede from the earth, so that it is now a quarter of a million miles away instead of a few-earth-diameters distance when it first went into orbit. During its life the moon has passed through a series of ever widening circles around the earth, sweeping up all the residual debris spread around the earth in the form of small satellites when Mars and the moon were formed. The impact of these satellite bodies with the moon caused many of the large craters on the moon's surface, and since the number of impacts was greater when the moon was near the earth, it is easy to see why most of the larger lunar craters are old ones. As the moon moved farther away so the concentration of ancient fragments of the earth decreased.

The latest calculations of the energy lost due to the tides indicate that the moon was very close to the earth about 1,700-million years ago—about one-third of the age of the earth. This figure assumes, however, that the present-day tidal friction has remained roughly constant throughout this period. It does not allow for the fact that in the earlier stages the tidal friction was probably much less than it is now, because the original land mass

Opposite: a total solar eclipse. Not only is the tidal friction produced by the moon and sun gradually causing the earth to rotate more slowly; it is also causing the moon itself to recede from the earth at a rate of a little under an inch a year. Scientists accordingly deduce that the moon was once very much closer to the earth than it is now

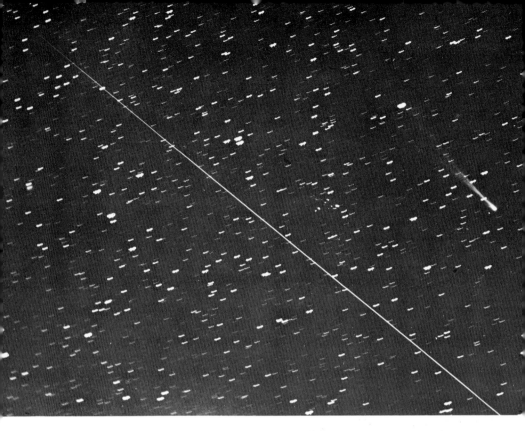

A 'shooting star', or meteor trail, appears in the night sky as a small meteor enters the earth's protective atmosphere and burns out. Only the remnants of a relatively few, large meteors survive the atmospheric friction and fall to the earth as meteorites. On an average day, some million meteors enter the atmosphere, yielding about ten tons of meteorites. (Also in the photograph is a distant comet–a mass of meteoritic rocks and dust, not burning but reflecting the sun's light as it follows a solar orbit)

The lunar crater Langrenus, about 115 miles in diameter, probably caused by the impact of a large meteor soon after the moon formed

had not yet been fragmented and eroded to produce the narrow channels which account for much of the tidal energy loss.

Properties of the core

The heavy material that sank towards the centre of the original molten earth has long been believed to be liquid iron under great pressure. This belief undoubtedly arose from the existence of iron meteorites, which could be accounted for by the break up of planetary bodies of similar origin to the earth. On this supposition the stony meteorites represent the mantle-rock type, and the iron ones the core. There are, however, other types of meteorites, and a more detailed examination of the meteorite evidence does not afford so clear-cut a picture as the simple contrast between core and mantle. However, there are many ways in which the original material could have been modified, so that it is not surprising that odd combinations of minerals are found in some cases.

The numerical evidence in favour of an iron core is provided by the estimates of density in the core, and of the earthquake-wave velocities that can be matched with those for shock waves passing through substances under corresponding pressures in the laboratory. There is an abrupt change in density from 5 to 9·7 at the boundary of the earth's core. The pressure at this point is about 1·4 megabars (more than a million times the atmospheric pressure at the earth's surface), and at this pressure iron (normally of density 7·9) would have at least the required density.

A more revolutionary attempt to account for the high-density core suggests that it is highly compressed hydrogen, in an atomic rather than normal gaseous-molecular state. Other suggestions hold that it consists largely of metallic liquid

Two meteorites, each about 12 inches across. Top: a stone meteorite which fell in Texas. Bottom: an iron, nickle-iron and olivine meteorite from Wyoming

forms of silicates, but the account embracing most of the evidence proposes that the core is iron with a mixture of lighter materials such as hydrogen, helium, carbon and silicon; that it is liquid; and that it is a good conductor of electricity.

Measurement and the mantle

Speculation about what the inside of the earth is made of has been continuing since the days when the belief in a flat earth gave way to the spherical concept of the Greek philosophers. With many who cared to think about the problem, a hollow earth was popular, and this was the model favoured by Jules Verne, when he made his intrepid band of explorers disappear down a geyser in Iceland to find a new world of adventure underground, finally to return on the upflow of the volcano Stromboli. Conan Doyle's Professor Challenger, on the other hand, subscribed to a solid earth, but supposed that it was an enormous living animal, rather like a sea-urchin in appearance, with a soft jelly-like body and a hard outer shell. It annoyed the Professor to visualize this vast animal, drifting slowly through space (presumably browsing on the ether) while human beings with their superior intellect were mere parasites camping on the animal's outer shell. The Professor was a practical man, and tested his theory by having a shaft dug eight miles into the earth. The jelly-like pulsating matter was reached, and for good measure an oil-man was hired to prod the animal with a drill.

Professor Challenger had approached the problem of what lies beneath us in a sensible manner that will no doubt one day be emulated in practice. It is known that the crust of the earth–about which we know a great deal, because it contains the rock layers that are all around us at the sur-

A fixed-leg oil-drilling platform in the North Sea. Much of our knowledge of the structure and composition of the earth's crust has been gathered by geologists while prospecting for oil

face, and because we dig and drill for minerals – is only about 20 miles thick. Although this is four times the greatest depth penetrated in oil-well drilling, it is not inconceivable that a sample of the mantle rock will eventually be obtained. Since the mantle occupies more than four-fifths of the earth's volume and constitutes nearly three-quarters of its mass, it is the most important component of the earth. At the present time we know of the mantle only what has been deduced from a comparatively small number of measurements, spread in history over the past few thousand years.

Eratosthenes, a Greek living in Alexandria *c.* 450 BC, is credited with the first authoritative calculation of the earth's size. His method – much the same as is used today – was to measure the distance between two points on the earth's surface. Eratosthenes noted that at midday the sun was directly overhead at Syene, since it shone straight down to

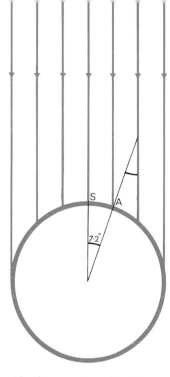

The figure constructed by Eratosthenes in attempting to calculate the earth's circumference. S locates the well at Syene, and A the tower at Alexandria.

the bottom of a well, while at Alexandria, a few hundred miles down the Nile, the sun was about seven degrees off the vertical. The distance between the two towns was then a fiftieth of the earth's circumference. The distance was allegedly determined by the number of days taken by a camel to travel between the two observing points, and a most regular camel it must have been, since Eratosthenes' result of 23,000 miles is close to the modern value.

A figure for the earth's mass was not obtained until many centuries later. Newton had first to formulate his law of gravitation, and Cavendish perform his experiment to determine the constant allowing the numerical value of the attraction between two bodies to be calculated. Thereafter, by working out the moon's velocity in orbit and the radius of its orbit, it was possible to calculate the earth's mass. The average density of the earth was found to be 5·5. Since the crustal rocks had a density of about 2·8, it was immediately apparent that, far from the earth being hollow, it had a high internal density. The core accounts for most of this high value, for the density in the mantle ranges from 3·2 at the junction with the crust, to about 5 at a depth of 2,000 miles, where the liquid core begins.

Careful measurement of the relative movements of the earth and moon show small perturbations of the main orbital paths. These are explained by the fact that mass inside the earth is not uniformly distributed. The 'precession of the equinoxes' is dependent on the moment of inertia of the earth, and its observation has provided a figure for the moment of inertia and hence an idea of the way in which the mass is distributed.

The combination of size, mass, and moment of inertia allowed the approximate composition of the earth to be calculated, but the details of the change of density with depth, and in particular, the existence of a liquid core, were provided by the probing of the earth's inside by means of earthquake waves. About sixty years ago Professor Mohorovičić, working in what is now Yugoslavia, noticed that two separate velocities, differing by about 25 per cent, were observed when recording the waves travelling outwards from earthquake centres within a radius of a few hundred miles. He rightly concluded that the slower waves had travelled through the earth's crustal rocks, and that the later, faster waves had penetrated the crust and had travelled in a harder, tougher rock layer which underlaid the crust. This underneath layer is the mantle, and the junction between crust and mantle was named the Mohorovičić Discontinuity, or in its modern shortened form, the Moho. The Moho may represent a sudden change from one type of rock to something with a different chemical composition. It may on the other hand represent a physical change in rock properties due to the increased pressure at depth. All that is really certain is that at a depth of about 20 miles beneath the continents, there is a sudden jump of about 25 per cent in the speed of earthquake waves.

The speed of earthquake waves depends on the

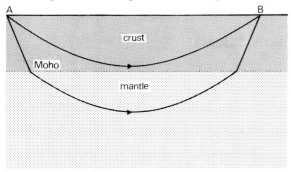

In 1909 the geophysicist Mohorovičić, while studying the records of a Balkan earthquake, noticed that shock waves passing below a certain depth suddenly speeded up. He concluded that this depth—which averages 20 miles beneath continental surfaces and 3 miles beneath the sea floor—marked the boundary between the earth's crust and a denser substratum, the mantle

33

elastic properties of the rocks in which the waves travel. By observing the waves at various distances from earthquake centres it is therefore possible to learn something about the rocks that exist deep down in the mantle. By combining the earthquake-wave measurements with the moment of inertia calculated from the moon's orbit observations, it is possible to conclude that a steady increase in density occurs in the mantle, so that this layer in the earth is probably uniform chemically, and the changes in wave velocity and density can be accounted for by increases in temperature and pressure with depth.

Two main types of earthquake waves can be observed in the initial shocks. The fastest travelling is the 'P' wave, which can move through either solid or liquid. The 'S' wave, which always arrives after the P wave, has a vibratory motion at right angles to its direction of travel, and cannot exist in a liquid, because a liquid has no rigidity to support the sideways motion. Liquids can only transmit compressional waves, which travel like a sound wave in air as a moving band of compressed material. The P waves from earthquakes can be followed right round the earth, and waves which have travelled through the mantle and core can be recorded at the antipodes. The S waves, on the other hand, peter out when followed to a point less than a third of the earth's circumference away from the earthquake origin. This is because the S wave which arrives at this point meets the liquid core and cannot be transmitted farther.

World-wide earthquake observing stations have been in operation for most of this century, and a vast number of observations has been collected. These allow the density at different depths to be calculated with some reliability, and form the

Of the two main types of shock wave emanating from earthquakes, the P (or 'principal') waves, capable of transmission through both solids and liquids, are unimpeded in their passage through the earth. The S (or 'secondary') waves, however, are invariably deflected at a depth of about 1,800 miles. Since it is known that S waves cannot pass through liquids, a largely liquid core is inferred

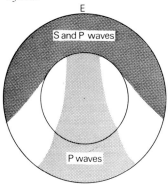

basis for the figures given earlier for the core and the mantle. There is some indication that inside the liquid core a smaller solid core exists, but more accurate observations are needed to establish this beyond doubt.

Earth and the other planets

The formation of the solar system by the cold accretion of particles of solid, liquid and gas in an interstellar dust cloud provides a reasonable explanation for the main features of the earth as we know it today. The moon can be satisfactorily accounted for, in spite of its abnormally low density, if we allow it to have escaped from a region centred on the present Pacific Ocean, where it left a scar which largely determines the extent of the oceans of the world. To keep the dynamics of the system. in order Mars must have left the earth with the moon when the earth melted due to radioactive heating, and rotated faster as the heavy iron core formed at its centre. Mars probably left before the core separation was completed, since its density of 4 suggests that something heavier than crust and mantle material is present. Mars may not prove to have a liquid core, and may well be a homogeneous mixture of mantle and crust. It would depend upon how the solidification process operated subsequent to departure from the earth.

The Venus–Mercury system could be similar to that of the earth and Mars. Venus and Mercury both have densities which approximate that of the earth, and therefore that of the primeval solid building matter of the solar system. However, Venus is closer to the sun than is the earth, and would experience a stronger attractive pull when it became molten through the radioactive action of Al^{26}. The separation of Mercury therefore

Pluto	·	3,680
Neptune		2,800
Uranus		1,790
Saturn		887
Jupiter		484
Mars	·	142
Earth	•	93
Venus	•	67
Mercury	·	36

Sun

The relative sizes of the planets of the solar system. The figures indicate distance from the sun in millions of miles

probably took place before any speed-up of rotation due to settling of heavy iron to the centre had occurred. This would account for Mercury's normal planetary density.

The meteorites are thought to be the remains of asteroids a few hundred miles in diameter, which have been shattered by collisions. The composition of the iron and stony meteorites is compatible with the cold-accretion origin. The larger planets—Jupiter, Saturn, Uranus—have low densities because they are farther away from the sun than the terrestrial group of planets. They receive far less heat and have therefore retained much of their hydrogen and helium, which the warmer inner planets could not keep. Methane and ammonia have been shown to exist on Jupiter by the study of spectra emitted. These larger outer planets may have concentrations of solid material beneath the cold dense cloud of gas, and if only they could move nearer the sun they might conceivably change into something like the earth as they shed their inhospitable outer atmospheres.

By inspecting the spectrum of the light reflected by a planet astronomers can gain information about the planet's chemical composition. Below: the matched spectra of (from top to bottom) the sun, Saturn, Jupiter and ammonia gas. The atmospheres of Saturn and Jupiter are evidently rich in ammonia. Opposite: photographs of Jupiter (top) and Saturn

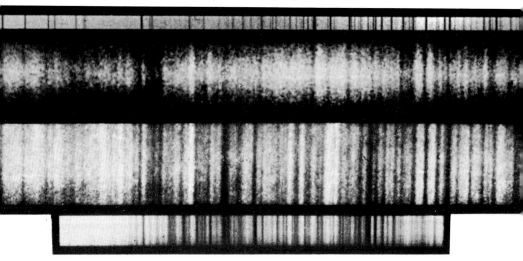

THE DRIFTING CONTINENTS   2

The continents, which collectively provide the
main evidence for the known geological history
of the earth, were originally made up of the
lighter rock that floated to the surface of the
molten earth to form the 20-mile-thick crust.
Molten rock rising up from the mantle has subsequently forced its way into the crust and many
other changes have taken place, but the basic
composition of the crustal material has remained
much the same ever since its separation from the
primeval planetary material.

There is some modern argument in favour of
a gradual and continual build-up of continents by
the accretion of material deposited on the ocean
floor. This material, carried along by a sideways
movement of the ocean floor, would be scraped
off under the margins of continents. Such a process in conjunction with the wearing down of
volcanic matter from inside the earth to provide
a continuous supply of sediment, could conceivably account for the fact that the continents oc-
cupy only one-third of the earth's surface, and
that they are formed of rocks unlike those in the
mantle. However, geological examination of continental rocks suggests that it is more probable

*Opposite: the earth as photographed
from the unmanned satellite* Lunar
Orbiter 4 *on 8 August 1967.
Africa, the Arabian Peninsula and
India can be distinguished through
the relatively sparse cloud cover.
The Arabian Peninsula is thought
to be gradually rotating in an anti-
clockwise direction towards Asia as
a result of movements in the underlying mantle rock*

that the continents have always been about the same size as they are now. Large stable 'shields' of continental rock exist which are more than 2,000-million years old, and these 'basement' rocks appear to underlie more recent continental rock formations.

The shaping of land surfaces

Although there may be some doubt about the origin of the continents, there is plenty of observational evidence about the situation that exists today. The land is continually being worn away and the spoil deposited to form flat layers of sediment which eventually consolidate to become new rock strata. Sun, wind, rain and extremes of heat and cold are relentless attackers of even the toughest rocks at the earth's surface. The high mountain tops are constantly subject to a destruction process based on the force exerted in narrow cracks when water freezes. Snow collecting in

Brecon Beacons in Wales—a landscape scooped out by ancient glacial action, as though by a giant with a great spoon. Pressures under a thousand feet of ice average about 30 tons per square foot—and ice cover in some parts of Greenland and Antarctica is about 2 miles thick

the cold, high places packs down under its own weight to form those great rivers of ice – the glaciers – that inch their way down the mountain slopes, gouging valleys out of the rock and depositing the rubble as a moraine when warm, melting conditions are reached.

Rain and melting snow and ice produce the torrents that carve away at the hillsides, their powers of erosion enhanced by the abrasive action of the sand and stones that they carry along with them. Even on the flatter ground, rivers chew away at their banks, meandering in a snake-like way because the cutting power of the water is greatest where it moves fastest at the outer side

A pair of glaciers in Greenland extending from their common source, a distant snow-covered plateau. While the rate of flow of Alpine glaciers rarely exceeds a foot a day, in Greenland and Alaska rates of over 100 feet a day have been recorded

Meanders and ox-bow lakes formed by the Mudjalik River in Alaska

An entrenched meander of the Colorado River in Utah

of a bend. In this way bends are gradually accentuated until the meanders join each other to leave ox-bow lakes of stagnant water. In millions of years a river will snake back and forth to produce a wide plain of freshly deposited material that started life in the mountains and has been ground up and sorted in the mill of the shifting river-bed.

The wind plays a part in the wearing down of mountains, since, when laden with abrasive sand particles, it can cut away at the hardest rock. The winds that blow over hot deserts pile up and shift the sand, so that the sand dunes move in waves across the land, while the individual grains of sand become rounded and sorted into groups of uniform size. One day these desert sands may be buried beneath thousands of feet of rock, and then the minute pores that exist between the sand grains could become a store-house for valuable deposits of oil or gas.

Sometimes large pieces of mountain are toppled by earth tremors originating deep in the crust.

Below left: sandstone eroded by water and wind near Wadi Timna in Israel

Below: sand dunes advancing before the wind in the Calanscio Sand Sea in Libya

There is a mountainside in Persia where a block of limestone a thousand-feet thick once slid for several miles, coming to rest in the valley with such force that it bent over on itself like the beginning of a giant Swiss-roll. While big earthquakes do not appear to occur very frequently, there is ample time for these earth movements alone to break down the highest mountains, for geological happenings are measured in units of millions of years. Any changes that can be observed to be taking place today must be magnified a myriad times in order to see what the forces of erosion have achieved in the total geological history of the earth. The earth movements have an effect on the land in addition to that of destruction. A slight tilting of a continental land mass can submerge former land a few hundred feet beneath the sea, where it may become the foundations of new sedimentary rock layers.

The laying of sediments

The fine material into which all mountains are converted when the wind and rain and ice, helped by acid waters from vegetation, have done their work in the course of millions of years, eventually finds its way down to the sea. There may be temporary resting places at the foot of a glacier or on an alluvial plain, but most of the ground-up rock finds its way to the bottom of the shallow seas that surround the continents. When the rivers disgorge their spoil into the sea the heavier and larger grains are the first to be deposited, so that the process of erosion and deposition causes a separation of the original rock material into its component parts. The clays and chalks and shales, the limestones and sandstones that help to make the surface scenery so interesting and so different have all been formed by the deposition in shallow

Opposite top: the delta or 'Burning Tree' of the Colorado River forming and reforming in the silt deposits at the river's mouth. Bottom: sharply defined layers of sedimentary rock — sandstone, limestone and shale — in cliffs at Barry in south Wales

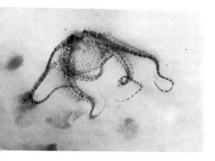

X-ray photograph of a small marine fossil preserved in shale from Devonian times, about 370-million years ago

The fossil remains of corals, lamp shells and trilobites preserved in a slab of limestone formed about 400-million years ago on the sea-bed near what is now Dudley, in Worcestershire

water of ground-up rock from the land. They have been deposited as sedimentary rocks. Some have been compacted by pressure and heat, while others have been cemented together by calcium-carbonate and similar materials brought down to the sea together with the mud and sand that the rivers carry. Some rocks contain the fossil remains of animals that once lived in the shallow seas, and these fossil remains provide some of the clues that allow rocks in different parts of the world to be compared and assigned to definite periods in the earth's long geological history.

Many different types of sedimentary rock exist, reflecting the quality of the material brought down by the rivers, and of the environment that existed at the time that the sediments were deposited. At any given period in geological time sedimentary rocks will be produced in shallow seas in many different parts of the world, and fossil evidence and other methods of dating the rocks will show that they belong to the same geological period, even though the rock material may be limestone in one place and shale in another. Some rock layers extend for hundreds of miles because they were deposited in a large shallow sea, but in many instances the character of the rock changes within quite short distances. What is porous rock, with a good potential for holding oil in one place, can change to an impermeable shaly rock within a mile or two. This is not surprising when one reminds oneself that what happened millions of years ago is similar to what goes on along our coasts today. Miles of sandy beach, which will eventually become sandstone rock, gives way to mud in those places where a small river joins the sea. In tropical waters, long narrow belts of fringing coral reefs are the beginnings of limestone rock layers. Sometimes the sedimentary rocks are thousands of feet thick, while in neighbouring areas that were never submerged there is no sedimentary deposit at all

The earth's crust is very sensitive to quite small changes in the mantle. Such changes, if they cause tilting of the crust, may transform land into sea or produce a wrinkle that creates an underwater depression. These depressions on a large scale produce the really thick layers of sediment in the world, since a downward warping of the crust pulls the rivers in its direction. But a wrinkle of the crust could produce a mountain five miles high just as easily as an underwater trap for sediments. In the course of time, therefore, newly formed sedimentary rocks may be raised or tilted to produce new land, and the shells of sea creatures will be found thousands of feet above sea-level in mountain rocks that are being worn away by rivers and glaciers.

The erosion and deposition of the continental rocks goes on continuously, in much the same way that the soil of a garden is dug over every year. Many sedimentary rocks that we see today have themselves been produced by the erosion of other sedimentary rocks. However, there must have been a time when the whole process began, when the attack of the forces of erosion was on the original material forming the crust. Examples of this attack may be seen in many parts of the world, since by no means all crustal rocks are sedimentary. Igneous rocks, formed by the solidification of molten rock material, are commonplace near the many volcanoes that perforate the earth's surface, and in the large granite formations that exist in many countries. Some granite rocks are the result of recrystallization rather than of the disgorging of molten rock from below the surface. A large class of 'metamorphosed' or

The rock cycle, illustrating the relationship between igneous, sedimentary and metamorphic rocks. The main processes involved are (1) erosion; (2) heat, pressure, and solution; (3) compaction and cementation; and—to an uncertain extent— (4) deep burial with melting

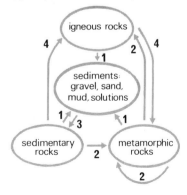

altered rocks exists in the earth's crust, the origin of which is partly igneous and partly sedimentary. The change in character occurs because of the pressure caused by the weight of overlying rocks, which may produce platy material like slate, and because of the temperature, which causes hot fluids to permeate the rock, often allowing enriched components of the original rock to crystallize out. Sandstones change into quartzites, and veins of gold or tin may be produced during the heating process. Limestones may be converted to marble, the grained appearance of which suggests that a process of near melting together with flow of liquid to fill up the cracks has taken place.

Sea-water and wealth

The combination of the metamorphic processes and the erosion and redeposition as sedimentary rocks, aided by outpourings of molten lava, have produced the enormous variety of rocks that can be seen at the earth's surface or be discovered by mining. The millions of years in which changes have been wrought on the original rocks has had a more important effect. Many minerals have been concentrated, so that a great part of the refining needed to produce pure metals has already been performed by natural processes. Valuable deposits are produced when shallow inland seas evaporate. In the course of some 10- or 20-million years thousands of feet of salt have been formed in many parts of the world where the land has slowly sunk and the evaporating lake has been continually replenished from the sea. As the salts become concentrated, first one chemical, then another, crystallizes out, so that, as well as the familiar rock salt, thick layers of nitrates, bromides and iodides are deposited.

Some sediments are rich in decayed plant life,

Opposite: a granite dome in the Yosemite National Park in the United States. Left: Ayer's Rock, a remarkable sandstone formation near the centre of the Australian continent. Below: a Gemini-V photograph of Lake Niriz surrounded by large salt marshes and cradled in the Zagros Mountains of southern Iran. The pinkish-white flats to the right indicate useful potassium-chloride deposits. (The ruins of the ancient city of Persepolis are visible in the bottom right-hand corner)

Opposite top: terraced sedimentary outcrops in Iran caused by a local tilting of the surface rock through an angle of ninety degrees. Bottom: diagram showing how oil traps are formed by movements in the earth's crust

An exposed salt dome in Heligoland. Such upwellings of salt in the earth's crust—which usually do not break the surface—mark the positions of ancient inland seas and are commonly associated with important oil and natural-gas fields.

and form thick layers of peat or coal. These fresh-water fossil fuels can be seen in process of formation today, but the coal deposits that are being mined have taken many millions of years to mature and are not being replaced in times measured in human life spans. Oil is formed when plants and animals fall to the sea-bed and decay to form the mixture of hydrocarbons that constitutes petroleum. The traces of oil are squeezed out of the mud in which they form until they collect in porous limestones and sandstones—provided a suitable fold or other form of trap exists in the layer of rock so that the lighter oil may be held floating on a water seal underneath. The concentration and collection process probably

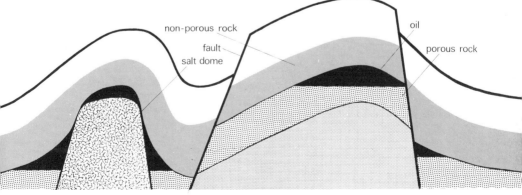

non-porous rock

oil

fault

porous rock

salt dome

takes millions of years, so that, as with coal, the world's supply of oil as far as the present generation is concerned is limited, and once used up will not be replenished for millions of years.

The production of all the concentrates of minerals, metals, fuels and building materials has been achieved by the gradual wearing away of old rocks and laying down of new ones. These concentrates of mineral wealth are being rapidly mined at the present time, and must be exhausted one day. For the next hundred years or more, the ingenuity of geologists and geophysicists will keep pace with man's demands, and chemists and metallurgists will devise means of working less concentrated ores. There will be no need to despair, moreover, when all the land sources of necessary materials are used up, since, during the continuous cycles of erosion and deposition of the land, vast quantities of all kinds of minerals are swept down to the sea. A vast mineral wealth held in solution in the earth's 300-million cubic miles of sea-water is awaiting recovery. The total quantity of salts in all the oceans is 54,000-million-million tons. Although more than three-quarters of this is common salt, there are large quantities of metals, for example 16,000-million tons of aluminium, 5,000-million tons of copper, 110,000-million tons of phosphorus. Magnesium is even more plentiful, at 2,000-million-million tons, and is already in commercial production from sea-water in places where cheap electricity is available. Another element extracted economically from sea-water is bromine, of which a total of 100-million-million tons is available. Bromine is used extensively in the oil industry to form part of the tetra-ethyl-lead anti-knock additives that are used to increase the octane rating of petrol for high-compression engines.

Opposite top: natural gas—which is often associated with oil or coal—ignited for safety, bubbling to the surface about a hundred miles off the Yorkshire coast after a drilling rig had broken adrift in a gale. Bottom: a flare proclaiming the first major gas strike in British waters in the North Sea (December 1965)

It is unlikely that any other minerals will be obtained from sea-water until very cheap power becomes available. However, in perhaps fifty years' time, when nuclear power should be taking over from fossil fuels, we shall probably be working down towards some of the elements that are present in lower concentrations. Titanium, for example, is becoming popular for light-alloy work, and the sea's resources of 1,500-million tons may one day be tempting enough for an economic process to be developed. Uranium itself has been the subject of investigation by the British Atomic Energy Authority, which believes that some of the sea's 5,000-million tons could be harvested at only a few times the cost of mining and concentrating it on land. The entire world's present energy requirements—involving the consumption of 2,000-million tons of oil, and 2,300-million tons of coal a year—could be met by modern nuclear plants fuelled with about 3-

Sea-water, treated chemically at this plant on the coast of California, precipitates magnesium chloride, from which pure magnesium is recovered

Economic large-scale extraction of all the many minerals dissolved in sea water will probably depend on the development of cheap atomic power. Left: an atomic reactor in course of construction at Oyster Creek, Long Island

million tons of uranium, so that the quantity available in the sea provides a useful reserve for several centuries.

Some concentration of minerals has taken place on the sea-bed in addition to the accumulations on the continents and on the continental shelves. It has been known for a long time, from results of dredging on the floor of the deep oceans, that layers of manganese nodules exist. These nodules are about the size of potatoes and contain the metals manganese, cobalt and copper, and will be an economic source of these metals when the more cheaply exploitable sources on land have been used up. The mechanism by which the metals are concentrated from their dilute solution in sea-water into the nodules is not yet known, but research into this problem may soon lead to the devising of man-made equipment for performing the extraction under controlled conditions. There is much also to be learned from a study of animals in the sea, since many of them are also capable of gathering valuable metals from sea-water. The ascidian, a sea-worm, for some reason concentrates vanadium into itself. The vanadium turns up later in crude oil, and is troublesome because it causes erosion of gas-turbine blades. The lobster extracts copper from sea-water, either because it likes this metal, or because it puts it to one side because copper is poisonous. Whatever the reason, many sea animals have perfected ways of concentrating minerals. By copying the methods of these animals it should be possible to devise adsorption and filtration processes for operation on a large scale.

Sometimes nature does the work herself. Right: manganese nodules—economically the most important metallic sediment accumulating on the ocean bottom—at a depth of 17,000 feet. In the Pacific Ocean alone these nodules are still forming at a rate of some 10-million tons a year

Informative shock waves

In the meantime geophysicists have developed methods for locating the concentrated supplies of valuable minerals on land, and similar geophysical tools have been adapted by oceanographers to

study the geological formations that exist under the sea. During the past few decades a great deal has been discovered about the rock layers that exist under the sea-floor, and it has been established that the oceans, where the water is between two and three miles deep, are geologically quite different from the continents. We might expect this if we accept the theory of the removal of Mars and the moon from the earth. Indeed it was the deep-ocean geophysical investigations that led to a reappraisal of the evidence relating to the history of the earth, and which has made this theory, together with that of continental drift, more acceptable to geologists and geophysicists.

On land we learn about rock layers by examining them at the surface, where they 'outcrop'. By following a rock layer at exposures of the rock in quarries, in road- or rail-cuttings, or in shallow water wells, it is possible to deduce the form of

Modern prospecting for metals. The torpedo-shaped magnetometer being towed by the helicopter can detect ore deposits by their effect on the earth's magnetic field. Electrically conducting ores lying up to 500 feet and more underground may be detected by inducing currents in the ore deposits

Above: a depth-charge explodes during seismic tests to determine the sub-structure of the sea-bed. Shock waves produced by such explosions are refracted and reflected in various ways by the materials they pass through before being picked-up by detectors which measure their time of travel (see diagram opposite). Right: a detector, or geophone, about to be lowered overboard

the layers deeper underground. In the search for minerals, geological forecasts are checked by borings into the ground, and finally by shafts of sufficient size to enable the mineral to be mined. Shafts and bore-holes are expensive, and in order to lessen the cost of exploration, geophysical methods of probing into the ground have been developed. The most powerful of these methods is to send out sound-waves and record the time these take to travel down to various rock layers and be reflected back to the surface. This 'seismic' method is a small-scale version of the earthquake-wave studies used to discover the earth's main features, such as its crust, mantle and core. The source of the sound-waves is usually an explosion, and with charges of a few hundred pounds it is possible to probe into rock layers ten miles below the sea surface.

The diagram on this page shows several different possible paths for sound-waves sent out by the explosion at A. The 'direct' wave on the surface layer goes horizontally to the detector at B, and it is obvious that it will always arrive before the reflected wave ACB, because it always has a shorter distance to go. The 'refracted' wave travels along the path ADEB. Part of the path is down and up, AD and EB in the top layer, but the main part is the horizontal section DE in the underneath layer. The wave travelling along AD is refracted at the boundary between the two layers, just as light is refracted or bent as it passes from air into a glass prism. The sound-wave is bent again at E to travel upwards to the top layer and back to the detector at B, in a perfectly symmetrical manner. Now, although the path ADEB is longer than either that of the direct wave AB or that of the reflected wave-path ACB, it is not necessarily longer in travel time. If the horizontal distance DE is great enough, the time saved in the fast layer will more than make up for the down and up time in the slower top layer.

Diagram to illustrate the seismic method, explained in detail in the text on this page

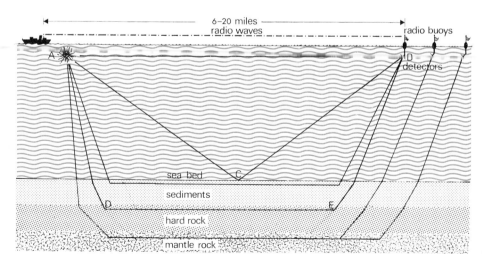

In order to make use of these refracted waves, several shots are fired at different distances and the travel times of the sound-pulses are plotted against the distance AB between shot and detector. At short distances it is the direct wave that is recorded, and this enables the speed of travel in the top layer to be determined. Beyond a certain distance the refracted waves reach the detector first, and from them the velocity of sound in the underneath layer is calculated. The travel time for the refracted wave is made up of the constant intervals AD and EB during which the sound-waves go down to the fast layer and back again, and the horizontal section DE where the travel time increases proportionately as DE is increased.

Deep-sea seismic results have revealed two main differences between oceans and continents. In the first place, the crustal rocks under the ocean floor have a thickness of only a few miles instead of the 20-mile thickness found by Mohorovičić for the continents. Secondly, the crustal rocks are not a complicated assortment of sedimentary and igneous rocks, folded and eroded and redeposited as on land. Instead, as might be expected if the sea-floor has always been under water, the geological system is a very simple one, consisting of a few thousand feet of sediment, a harder layer (which might be volcanic lava, shale, or limestone), and a granite layer.

This seismic evidence relating to the crust beneath the oceans made it possible to look at the earth as a whole, instead of, as in the past, being concerned only with the one-third that forms the land. The new look at the earth makes it apparent that the continents are exceptional features and may be regarded as masses of lighter crustal rock embedded in the denser mantle. Although the continents tend to be concentrated on the side of

A geophysicist examines a seismogram, a recording of shock waves received from an explosion several miles away

the earth away from the Pacific Ocean they do not produce an imbalance. If they did, the earth, spinning on its axis, would disintegrate. The 20-mile-thick light crustal layer under the continents just balances the combination of 3 miles of seawater, 4 miles of crust under the oceans and 13 miles of mantle rock, so that if one could take cores 20-miles deep anywhere on the earth's surface, they would all weigh the same. Another way of looking at this balance is to think of the continents as giant icebergs floating in the mantle rock. In order to achieve sufficient buoyancy they have to have a large part of their bulk submerged below the level of the crust-mantle interface beneath the oceans.

Part of the unsubmerged eighth of a colossal Antarctic iceberg. Many scientists believe that there is a useful analogy to be drawn between icebergs and continents. Just as icebergs float in the sea so continents may be thought of as floating partially submerged in the plastic material of the mantle

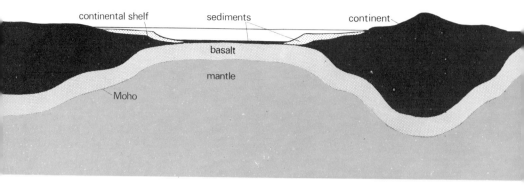

continental shelf   sediments   continent

basalt

mantle

Moho

Above: diagram showing the relative thicknesses of the earth's crust under continent and ocean (for clarity, the vertical scale is much exaggerated). Below: further evidence that the continents are floating on the mantle: the Baltic lands, no longer weighed down by extensive ice cover, have, since the last ice-age, risen en bloc by up to 1,000 feet (figures in the diagram are in metres). Opposite: a representation of the theory, proposed in 1912 by Alfred Wegener, that the present continents originated in the break-up of a single super-continent about 200-million years ago. In principle, if not in detail, Wegener's theory of continental drift is today generally accepted

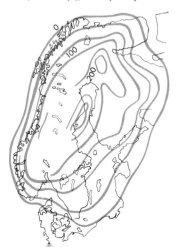

There is good evidence that, although the mantle is solid rock as far as earthquake-wave behaviour is concerned, it can act as a supporting fluid. For example, coral atolls are formed by the sinking of their parent volcanoes into the sea-bed. Again, the slow rise of Scandinavia is the result of the removal of the heavy load of ice that weighed the land down during the last ice-age. If the continents are floating on the mantle, it is not difficult to imagine them moving sideways as well as up and down. The possibility of relative movement of the continental masses is the crux of Wegener's hypothesis of continental drift.

Continental-drift theory

The theory, which has also been put forward by others independently of Wegener, is that the earth's land surface was formerly one big continent, which split up into the separate units that exist today by a slow process of drifting apart. The gradual unfolding of this primitive land mass is shown in the three stages as depicted by Wegener himself, and there is no doubt that his convincing series of pictures is one of the main reasons why so many people felt that there must have been some truth in the hypothesis.

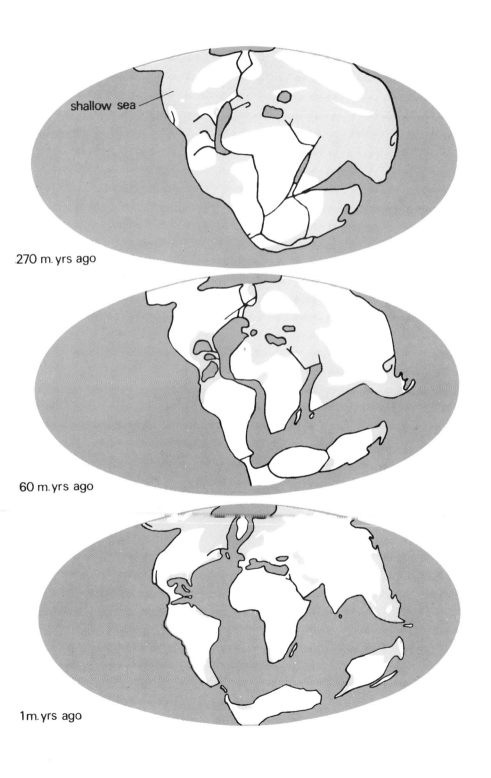

shallow sea

270 m. yrs ago

60 m. yrs ago

1m. yrs ago

The latest reconstruction of the land masses on opposite sides of the present Atlantic Ocean, by the Cambridge University Geophysics Department, shows a surprisingly good fit, much better than would be expected from a chance similarity in shape. The fitting is made at the edge of the continental shelf, which is the true boundary to a continent, not at the present-day coastline, which has been used in some past reconstructions.

Even with the true shape of the continental blocks known, and with the mountain ranges ironed out, a perfect fit is not necessarily to be expected, because remnants of the original land masses may have been left behind. Madagascar, for example, appears to be a vestige that used to be attached to India on the one side and Africa on the other, and the oddments of islands, such as the Seychelles and Mauritius, which contain continental-type rocks, are available to fill up gaps and make a neat fit to the continents of Australia, India and Africa, which are supposed to have drifted apart. In the Atlantic parts of the Mid-Atlantic Ridge, winding approximately midway down the ocean from north to south, would provide a useful make-up of material to account for any ill fitting between the present east and west shores.

It was not, of course, merely the shape of opposing coastlines that appealed to the geologists who favoured the drift hypothesis. Many of the rock layers were similar on both sides of the Atlantic, or in the various coastlines that were joined together in the Indian Ocean. The mountain ranges also, while bearing no relation to each other in their present orientation, often appeared as continuous folds of the earth's crust when looked at in the light of Wegener's assemblage. Such lines of folding can be followed through the

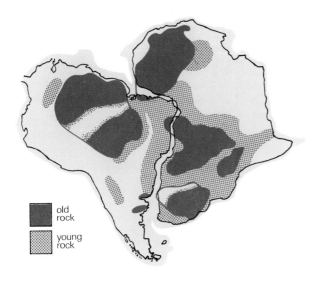

old
rock

young
rock

*The distribution of old (over 2,000-
million years old) and young rock
in South America and Africa provides one of several grounds for
believing that the two continents
were once parts of a single land mass.
This land mass, which has been
named Gondwanaland, is thought to
have included also Antarctica,
Australia, Madagascar and the
Arabian and Indian peninsulas. The
remaining land masses of the
northern hemisphere are thought to
have derived from a second adjacent
supercontinent, Laurasia*

eastern side of the United States and Newfound-
land and over to Scandinavia; or from the Atlas
Mountains of North Africa to Venezuela; or
again, from the Cape of Good Hope to Argentina.
Not only do the mountain ranges appear as continuous when the continents are pushed together
in the form of the proposed original land mass,
but they are mountains of similar rocks belonging
to the same geological age groups. This is shown
by the microscopic composition of the rocks and
by the fossils that they contain.

It must be remembered, when considering
similarity of fossils, that some of the animals that
form the fossils were widespread, and others were
able to move about quite readily, so that it is to be
expected that they will be found in countries
separated by vast oceans. This point is emphasized
by cases in which similar fossils are found where
not even the most generous imagination could
have produced contiguous continents in the past.
However, biologists have generally been in favour

either of continental drift, or of some form of land-bridge connection which has subsequently foundered, in order to explain the distribution of animals and plants in the world today. Even if continuous strips of land did not exist across the present-day oceans – and the great concentration of ocean soundings undoubtedly rules out this possibility – there were certainly quite extensive lines of island stepping-stones at one period in the Pacific, for their position is marked by the flat-topped sea-mounts and atolls. Migration from atoll to atoll is no doubt considerably more likely than migration over thousands of miles of open ocean, so that chains of islands would provide a useful biological link between continents. For some animals, as the Kon-Tiki expedition demonstrated, drifting on tree-trunks is a possible method of traversing great stretches of ocean, and this method could explain many of the curious distributions that have been adduced as facts favourable to the drift hypothesis. But this does not mean that it will explain everything; there remains plenty of good evidence which can be better accounted for by drifting of the continents themselves.

The record of past climates

If the continents have wandered, they will have changed their positions relative to the poles and the equator as well as to each other. Since climates in different parts of the world have distinct peculiarities, there should be a whole host of anomalies in the rocks that were laid down in past geological ages. According to Wegener, there was a movement of land away from the South Pole; not only would this have been accompanied by a drifting apart of individual pieces of land, which would show up in the geological,

Opposite: the geological time scale (figures indicate millions of years ago). The Pre-Cambrian Era represents at least 80 per cent of elapsed geological time: the oldest known rocks were formed about 3,000-million years ago. The Pliocene, Miocene, Oligocene, Eocene and Palaeocene are epochs of the Tertiary Period. The Quaternary Period extends over the past million years, all but the last 40,000 years belonging to the Pleistocene Epoch

biological and geographical similarities already mentioned, but also the older rocks in these lands would show signs of the rigorous climate to which they had been exposed in the past.

There are many examples, both in the kind of rocks and in the way they are laid down, to show that large changes of climate have occurred in many parts of the world. It is possible, of course, that the world has warmed up and cooled down as a whole, and that this has been the prime cause of different climatic environments. This alone does not, however, appear adequate to explain the observed facts, because it leads to a picture of impossibly conflicting world climates when the ages of the rock deposits are considered. The evidence from certain Indian rocks might, for example, indicate a cold climate at the same time in the earth's geological history that the west African climate was apparently quite normal.

A more drastic process which could account for anomalies in climate might be a change in position of the land masses as a whole relative to the earth's axis of rotation. The earth's crust would then be pictured as sliding around on an inside core like a loose outer skin, so that land previously at the poles might move towards the equator. There is some evidence that this polar wandering might occur, but it is certainly not enough on its own to account for all the changes that have obviously occurred in the climates of the past.

Geologists recognize periods of past glaciation by the many signs that are left behind by large sheets of moving ice. There is very little doubt about the evidence, because it can be checked against present-day glaciation in the Alps or the polar regions. In Carboniferous times, some 250-million years ago, parts of Argentina, South Africa, Madagascar, southern India and Australia

1 m
Pliocene
Miocene
Oligocene
Eocene
Palaeocene
70 m

Cretaceous

130 m

Jurassic

180 m

Triassic

225 m

Permian

270 m

Carboni-
ferous

350 m

Devonian

400 m

Silurian

440 m

Ordovician

500 m

Cambrian

600 m

Pre-
Cambrian

A rock surface in South Africa scored by glacial action in Permian times. Similar evidence of early Permian glaciation has also been discovered in Brazil, India and Australia, suggesting that the land masses involved were once close to-gether in the vicinity of the South Pole

were all covered with ice. This would be expected if these various lands were huddled together as part of Wegener's original continent, and if what is now Mozambique was at the South Pole. Since Patagonia, Indonesia and New Zealand missed this particular glacial period, a simple extension of the Antarctic ice, or a simple polar movement to the north, will not explain the facts.

The Antarctic continent formed part of the glaciated land mass in Carboniferous times, but at a later date it must have had a much warmer climate, because coal measures were laid down in Permian times. An interesting indicator of old climates is a particular kind of sandstone. In the first place, this material indicates desert conditions, because it is formed by the cementing together of wind-blown sand grains. A careful examination of the fine structure of the rock and the distri-bution of grains of various sizes enables the pre-vailing wind-direction to be ascertained. Now, the pattern of winds that blow across the earth's surface is partly determined by the axis of rotation of the earth, and therefore the direction of wind in the past as shown by the sand can be related to the orientation and latitude of the ancient land mass.

Typical of hot climates are deposits of salts, formed by the evaporation of inland seas. Some-times these evaporite beds are found on the coast, where the present-day continent meets the ocean. The difficulty of explaining this type of obser-vation is intensified for those who do not accept continental drift by the discovery of similar beds on the continent on the opposite side of the ocean. The present active search for oil and minerals is providing more detailed knowledge of both sides of the Atlantic, and it is becoming possible to compare whole sequences of rocks penetrated by

the drill, rather than relying on the more limited information available by inspection at the surface. New similarities are coming to light, and these are all found in the old rocks up to Cretaceous times—about 100-million years ago—but from this period the rocks are dissimilar. This is exactly what would be expected if America and Africa originally parted company when Cretaceous rocks were being laid down, and the evidence is the stronger for the change from like to unlike. It might be possible to believe that similarity of climate and of available materials for forming sediments produced the same kind of rocks at about the same latitude on opposite sides of the ocean, but for this to have held good in the past and not during the more recent geological periods

Exposed coal seams in Antarctica dating from the Permian Period imply that the polar continent itself once entered warmer latitudes

does not make sense. However, so many different mechanisms may be active in controlling climate and the associated deposition of new rocks that it cannot be stated for certain that chance coincidences did not occur during one particular phase of geological history. The belief in continental drift will carry even greater conviction if and when, as a single coherent theory, it can account for many coincidences that otherwise require several different, rare and improbable explanations.

Another indicator of past climates is the existence of coral rock, because the polyp which grows to make the coral will only live in warm water. Coral rock found in the frozen north of Canada demonstrates that the American continent must have been much farther south at one period of geological history than it is today. Such climatic evidence is supported by a comparatively

Fossil corals found in the bed of the Ohio River at Jeffersonville

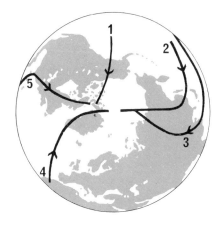 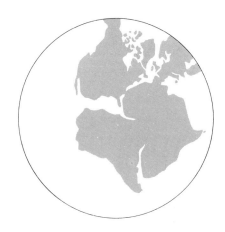

recent type of measurement involving a magnetic method of determining the latitude in which sedimentary rocks were originally deposited. The large accumulation of magnetic measurements of old rocks is beginning to lend numerical precision to the rather intangible evidence formed by estimates of past climates. There appears to be little doubt that considerable change has taken place in the position of the magnetic poles during the past 3,000-million years, and that there must have been both rotation and relative movement of the continents to explain the different directions in which rocks from various parts of the earth are found to be magnetized.

The direction of magnetization is generally determined by the orientation of the rocks when they were laid down, and this direction remains fixed in the rock independently of any tilting or folding that the rock subsequently suffers. If the rock is old and forms part of a drifting continent, the probability is that its magnetism will not point in the direction of the magnetic poles today. This simple picture is complicated, however, by the fact that the magnetic poles themselves move around, but by investigating rocks of all ages in

Measurements of 'fossil' magnetism in rocks in Japan (1), Europe (2), North America (3), Australia (4), and India (5) give very conflicting accounts of the apparent wanderings of the north magnetic pole during the past 200-million years. These differences may be reconciled, however, if it is supposed that the continents, before drifting to their present positions, were originally arranged as shown on the right

Modern cup corals (shown about twice natural size) taken from deep water in the Bay of Biscay

all parts of the world it should be possible to distinguish the polar movement from that of the continents. Results so far indicate that Australia was near the magnetic pole both in the earliest geological times and again later in the Carboniferous period, with an excursion to the equator in between. There is also evidence of a large angular separation between Europe and America since Cretaceous times, as Wegener proposed.

Drifting oil-fields

A good modern example of the practical value of studying the past history of the earth is the application of 'fossil magnetism' and continental drift to the search for oil. Some years ago it was noticed that there was a regular pattern in the world-wide distribution of oil-fields: most large oil-producing areas fall within the tropics. Considering first those oil-fields contained in recently deposited rocks (remembering that recent in the geological sense could be, say, up to 30-million years ago – which is not even one per cent of the earth's life) it is found that all lie in the tropical belt. It is only the oil found in older rocks that is in high northern or southern latitudes. These observations support the idea that petroleum is not only associated with marine sedimentary rocks, but also with those originally deposited in tropical climates. This can be confirmed by examination of the oil-bearing rocks themselves. Careful geological examination, using such pointers as the fact that certain corals can only grow in warm water, leads to the conclusion that oil accumulations are associated with tropical environments. Since many sedimentary rocks are formed under temperate conditions, it is possible to rule out a considerable volume of rock when looking for oil.

What, then, of oil-fields found outside tropical regions, such as, for example, those in Canada and Northern Russia? When the old rocks which house the oil are examined – rocks which may be a few hundred-million years old – signs are found which indicate that they too were formed in warm tropical conditions. A knowledge of the earth's past history indicates the possible ways of explaining how tropical conditions could have existed in the far north. One is that the earth periodically warms up to give quite different climatic conditions from those experienced today; the other explanation is continental drift.

The drift theory is confirmed in the case of oil-fields by taking magnetic readings from the old rocks that form the oil reservoirs, and thereby determining the latitudes in which the reservoir rocks were laid down. It is found that oil-fields in the Arctic wastes, or in the south of South America were originally in tropical latitudes, and have drifted to their present positions during the last few hundred-million years.

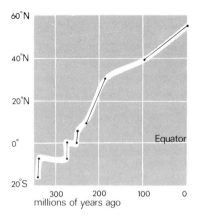

The latitude of the Dogger Bank at various periods in its history, calculated from the fossil magnetic record in the rocks

The North Sea provides a topical example of the use of the magnetic measurements in directing oil exploration to the most likely targets. The North Sea is far north of the tropics, so that productive oil deposits would not be expected. However, the coal measures of the Carboniferous rocks were laid down over 300-million years ago in tropical conditions, and examination of the Permian rocks, which are about 250-million years old, show that desert conditions existed when the Permian sediments were formed. By measuring the old magnetic-field directions in rocks of different ages found in Britain, it is possible to plot the drift of the Dogger Bank from below the equator 400-million years ago, to its present position at 55° North. If oil is generally found in rocks formed in the tropics, it is only the North-Sea rocks which are more than 200-million years old which are of interest. There is not much hope of oil, for example, under the North Sea opposite the Scottish coast, because although thick sediments exist, they are only about 100-million years old, and were already a long way from the tropics at the time they were laid down.

The theoretical studies of the earth's history, together with geological examination of the surface rocks, and probing and measuring with geophysical tools, allow us to reconstruct the environments at various times in the past. We learn more about the conditions under which mineral concentrations are formed, both by observing what processes are going on today, and by studying the reservoirs and mines that are exploited in different parts of the world. This makes it possible to locate valuable deposits which are deeper and more difficult to find than those that have satisfied man's demands in the past.

THE PLASTIC MANTLE 3

Wegener's continental drift hypothesis has suffered a great deal of criticism, especially at the hands of geophysicists who could not understand how a solid continent could possibly move in relation to an equally solid sea-floor. However, several plausible explanations for the movement of land masses across the earth's surface have now appeared.

If one strikes ice with a pick it will shatter, like any brittle substance. On the other hand, giant glaciers flow like rivers down the mountain sides of Switzerland; their movement can be measured by observing stakes driven into the ice. It is possible to produce sharp-edged fractures by hitting a piece of pitch with a hammer; yet that same piece of pitch, if left on a table for a few days, will spread into a flattish blob. In the case of both the ice and the pitch a different behaviour is observed depending upon whether the force acting on the material is applied rapidly or slowly. In a similar way, we can expect the properties of the mantle revealed by earthquake waves which act in seconds to differ from those demonstrated by expansive forces acting from within the earth over periods of millions of years.

It is the blocks of continental rock, twenty miles thick, that move slowly about the surface of the earth. The fluid on which these blocks move is the mantle, that layer of solid rock (as the earthquake-wave evidence implies) which reaches down from the base of the crust to a level about halfway to the centre of the earth. We know that the mantle is subjected to large forces; it wraps round the molten core of the earth, and must be conducting heat away from the core if the earth is cooling down. Even if the earth is near a point of equilibrium, neither heating up nor cooling down, heat is being generated in the mantle by the radioactive decay of uranium, potassium and thorium atoms. This heat has profound effects on the mantle, because it must escape to the earth's surface through the blanket of poorly conducting mantle rock.

Effects of convection currents

If we accept sources of heating in or below the mantle, and at the same time the possibility of plastic flow provided the movement is slow enough, then convection currents can be visualized in the mantle similar to those currents that can be seen circulating in a percolator of boiling coffee. These convection currents will have different effects at the earth's surface, depending on whether the particular part of the surface is above a rising current or one returning to the depths. For example, a rising current beneath a continent will tend to spread to right and left when it nears the surface and is deflected downwards; this will produce a tendency to split the continent, and could well be the explanation of the rift valleys which are such a distinctive feature of east Africa and the Red Sea. Measurements in the Red Sea suggest that splitting is still going on, and there

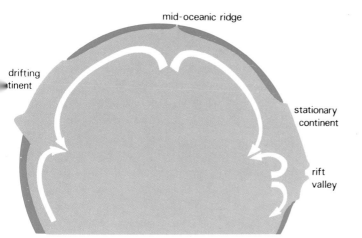

mid-oceanic ridge

drifting
ntinent

stationary
continent

rift
valley

is magnetic evidence that the Arabian peninsula is twisting, thereby pushing the Horn of Oman into the opposing Iranian coast. The effect of this convection current some hundreds of millions of years ago probably forced the southern triangle of India and Madagascar away from Africa.

An upwelling convection current could be operating under the Atlantic Ocean, causing the drifting apart of the Americas from Europe and Africa, which geological measurements suggest began about 120-million years ago. This convection current could have piled up the great mass of material which forms the Mid-Atlantic Ridge, that long mountain range that marks the median line between the opposite shores of the Atlantic. There is an interesting feature in the middle of the Ridge which supports the convection argument. This is a sharp valley which can be plotted by echo-sounder at many points, and could be the manifestation of a continuing splitting of the ocean-floor. The northern end of the Ridge is Iceland, and here frequent volcanic activity is associated with a pattern of multiple 'dykes', which consist of lava intruded upwards to fill north-south cracks in the rock which formed the original island. The rock layers to the east and

Major surface features and the drift of continents may be explained by circulating convection currents in the upper mantle. Tension caused by diverging up-currents would produce rift valleys and oceanic ridge systems. Converging down-currents would tend to compress, fold and raise the surface rock. Such currents, presumably resulting from radioactive heating and intermittent local melting in the otherwise solid mantle, could only move at an average rate of a few inches a year

west of Iceland are similar to each other, and were probably originally one, but they have been driven apart by the inexorable convection current of the mantle below, and each tear in the rock has been filled by molten lava which solidifies to form a dyke.

Since the earth's crust is only a thin skin 20 miles thick on a sphere 8,000 miles in diameter, it is not difficult to visualize mountain ranges as small wrinkles produced by quite small rearrangements in the mantle. Convection currents descending beneath a continent could be the cause of these wrinkles, and could account for the largest mountain ranges and deep-ocean trenches.

The ocean-floors, according to the mantle-convection theory, are always on the move, new ocean-bed being produced continuously by the central upwelling mantle current. When the moving ocean-floor meets a continent it tries to push the continent away but, if the continent has moved to a stable position above a descending portion of the current, the ocean-bed slides gently beneath the continental block. This has the same effect as a continuous roller on the floor of a bird-cage—all the debris of the ocean-floor, including sediments and volcanic islands, is swept beneath the continent to fuse eventually with the continental rocks.

According to one modern view the crustal rock of the ocean-bed continues round the cycle: downwards beneath the continent; horizontally at depth; then upwards again in the central part of the ocean. When the rock gets well below the crust it loses water and changes from one form of rock to another. It is proposed that the crustal rocks of the deep oceans (apart from the half-mile or so of sediment and volcanics) are composed of metamorphosed mantle rock and that

Opposite: volcanic activity in Iceland, an island that straddles the axis of the Mid-Atlantic Ridge

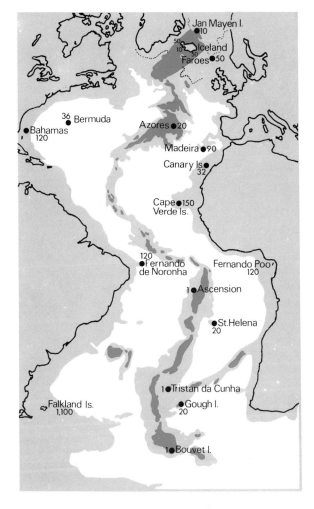

The ages of Atlantic islands suggest that the ocean-floors to east and west of the Mid-Atlantic Ridge are moving away from the axis of the ridge like a pair of gigantic conveyor belts. Ages are quoted in units of a million years

during circulation the mantle rock is regenerated by removal of water. If such continuous circulation of the sea-bed does occur then there will be no very old sediments anywhere on the ocean floor.

It has been suggested that the islands in the Atlantic have been carried sideways by the ocean floor, so that the farther away an island is from the middle of the Atlantic the older it will be. But there will be a limit to the age of the island, because it will, on this theory, eventually be pushed underneath the continental 'carpet' with the rest of the deep sea sediment. There will be a limit to the age of an island in the Atlantic in any case, if it is accepted that the splitting apart of Africa and America only started 120 million years ago. The Pacific Ocean, however, could be almost as old as the earth, and yet there may be movement of the sea-floor due to convection currents. In this case a further study of island ages should support the continuous movement theory.

The mantle rock may be too tough to allow continuous convection currents, and the continental movements could be accounted for by sporadic activity which has taken place due to an increase in the plasticity of the mantle caused by a softening of the rock by heat. It is not necessary for this softening to have taken place all over the earth at the same time. The evidence from continental drift, and the geological evidence accumulated about periods of active mountain building, are compatible with local heating over separate areas of the mantle at different times.

We have seen that seismic waves from earthquakes and explosions provide some pointers to the nature of the rock that forms the mantle. Unfortunately the seismic velocity in a particular rock is not discriminating enough to provide an unambiguous indication of rock type. For example, limestones are associated with velocities ranging from 10,000 to 22,000 feet per second for compressional waves; this range covers the velocities observed in many other rock types such as granites or shales. The velocity of the upper mantle is well above that of any limestone, but it can be matched by a few rocks which appear at the surface. For example, the peridotites, which are igneous rocks consisting mainly of iron-magnesium silicates, and which exist at a few places on the earth's surface, have seismic velocities compatible with those observed for the mantle. This type of rock appears as dunite in Australia, or as harzburgite in the Alps. It is possible that these occasional appearances do represent real outpourings of mantle, but they have not been incontrovertibly connected with the mantle, whose existence we still only deduce from the seismic velocities.

Although moon samples have been collected, returned to earth, and analyzed, it seems remarkable that we do not yet know what kind of rock forms the mantle. While we cannot yet drill through 20 miles of continent, we have already sunk boreholes 5 miles into the earth in the search for oil. In the Mohole project, which unfortunately is in abeyance, it was planned to drill from a ship in the Pacific at a place where the crustal rock covering the mantle was only about 20,000 feet thick. The difficulties of drilling over water that is 18,000 feet deep, and where it is not possible to anchor a drilling vessel, have already been mastered, so that it now only requires sufficient funds to enable rock samples to be collected from the mantle.

Mantle-rock samples could be subjected to tests under conditions simulating those inside the earth, and the feasibility of convection currents could then be ascertained. Rates of plastic flow could be measured, and the credibility of the various theories put forward to explain continental drift could be assessed. Since the mantle forms nearly three-quarters of the earth, the chemical analysis of mantle rock would provide good evidence of the mineral composition of the earth, and on the assumption of a universal cold-

accretion process, of the whole solar system.

One of the most important measurements that would be made on the mantle sample is a determination of its radioactivity. This would allow a great advance in all theories of the heat balance of the earth–whether the earth is gradually cooling, or whether the heat from radioactivity is more than keeping pace with the heat conducted

A coring drill bit, designed for the Mohole project, hanging in a derrick at the test site in Texas

out through the surface. It has been suggested that the earth is in a slow pulsating state with regard to its internal heat. The blanket of solid rock at its surface bottles up the radioactive heat formed throughout the mantle, causing zones of abnormally hot rock. These zones gradually creep towards the surface until a rapid loss of heat takes place due to vast outpourings of molten mantle material. After this loss of heat, the mantle settles down again to build up another zone of local melting, perhaps over many millions of years.

The low-velocity layer

There is modern evidence for nearly molten zones at depths of about 100 miles below the surface of the earth. As long ago as 1926 the geophysicist Beno Gutenberg noticed that the amplitude of compressional earthquake waves in the mantle decreased with abnormal rapidity in the distance range between 500 and 900 miles, while beyond 1,000 miles the amplitudes recovered. Although the velocity of earthquake waves normally increases with penetration into the mantle, this phenomenon could be accounted for by a layer of the mantle which slows down these waves. Today the existence of a 'low-velocity layer' in the upper mantle is well established. The velocity in

The low-velocity layer. Between 30 and 120 miles below the surface, earthquake P and S waves are both slowed down, presumably because the upper mantle rock, which is nearly melting in this region, is less rigid than elsewhere

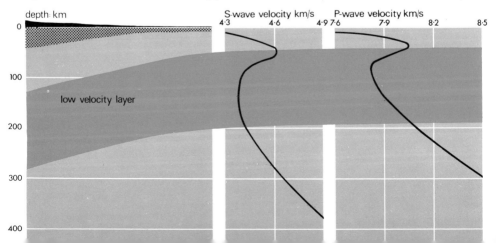

this layer, which lies between 50 and 150 miles below the surface, is less than that at the top of the mantle just below the Mohorovičić Discontinuity (Moho) and the Moho velocity is not attained again until a depth of 150 or 200 miles is reached.

Gutenberg studied both deep and shallow earthquakes and, since the effect of the low-velocity layer depends on whether the source of waves is above or below the layer, a certain blurring of the picture was apparent. This led to scepticism among seismologists; but today this has been removed by new evidence: the known locations of underground nuclear explosions has made it possible to place instruments at critical distances. When examined in detail, long-period surface waves behave exactly as though they are passing through a region of low velocity rather than a region in which velocity increases continuously with depth; and occasionally a very strong earthquake shock makes the earth vibrate like a struck bell. This happened with the Chile earthquake of 1960, and analysis of the components that made the 'tone' of the earth's ringing could only be explained by assuming a low-velocity layer in the earth's interior. Another interesting confirmation of Gutenberg's findings has been provided by the behaviour of transverse S waves which generally have wavelengths larger than those of their fellow compressional P waves. This could be due to poor transmission of the short S waves in a soft low-velocity layer. S waves are not transmitted at all by liquids and this seemed to suggest that the low-velocity layer might well be somewhat more fluid than the surrounding material.

The low-velocity layer occurs at depths of between 30 and 150 miles beneath the oceans, but is rather deeper—between 75 and 170 miles—beneath the continents. Calculations based on heat-flow through the surface of the earth and on the conductivity of rock, together with reasonable assumptions as to the radioactive content of the upper mantle, lead to the conclusion that rock in the low-velocity layer should be near its melting point. These calculations are not exact, but must be fairly accurate, since they confirm the hint, provided by the S-wave results that, in the low-velocity layer, rock is much more plastic than normal. Below 200 to 300 miles the effect of pressure on the melting point of the mantle material takes the rock back once more to the really solid state, as is indicated by earthquake-wave behaviour and also by the fact that earthquakes do occur as deep as several hundred miles below the low-velocity layer.

One of many fissures which appeared in the streets of Valdivia, Chile, during the catastrophic earthquake of 1960

The discovery of the low-velocity layer, even without the support of physical tests on samples of the mantle to determine what plastic flow is possible, may tell us what has been happening in the past. The layer should creep gradually upwards, because conduction is not adequate to remove all the heat being produced in the mantle. Where the nearly liquid layer approaches the surface, volcanic activity will increase enormously. A large squeezing-up of low-velocity-layer material to form batholiths, analogous to the formation of salt plugs, may take place and in turn these great intrusions may cause folding and sideways movement in the crust. In any case, this is the time when large horizontal movements are possible, and this is also probably the time when the convection currents play their main part.

A hump-backed mountain in Iran, the result of folding under stresses imposed by mantle convection

Calculations show that convection currents, confined to the upper few hundred miles of the mantle, could take their driving force from the estimated amount of radioactive energy in the mantle. Long periods of quiescence could be expected between periods of violent activity. It could be that channelling of the upward movement of the low-velocity layer is necessary to concentrate the available heat and that periodical 'heat attacks' on the earth are confined to lines or zones of activity.

One of the difficult things to explain is why continental drift only took place comparatively recently, during the past few hundred-million years of the earth's history. The English geophysicist Keith Runcorn has suggested that the earth's core has been growing as a result of gradual precipitation of iron from the mantle to the core. It is difficult to account for an increasing core without postulating a cold origin of the earth by the accretion of small meteorite-like masses. On the other hand, the old idea of an originally molten earth, which on cooling formed a thin crust of light material and at the same time precipitated its iron core, is simple and straightforward. There is some practical evidence that the core may have changed in size during geological time. Such a change, affecting the earth's moment of inertia, would cause a change in the speed of the earth's rotation. The picture is complicated by the tidal interaction of the moon with the earth. However, if it were possible to measure both the length of the day and the length of the month at different geological periods, any changes in moment of inertia should be calculable. It appears that the coral polyp, which builds the vast coral reefs, accumulates new material so quickly that daily growth-rings (comparable with annual tree-

Study of the daily growth rings on ancient corals may provide scientists with useful clues to changes in the earth's rotation and the length of the year in past eras

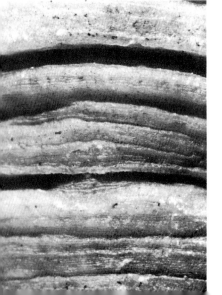

rings) can be seen. Provided enough seasonal change occurred, it should be possible to use the polyp to count the number of days in a year, and if any tidal effect altered growth characteristics–which it may well have done–a monthly or fortnightly count should also be feasible. Preliminary results, if confirmed, would seem to imply a change in the earth's moment of inertia in the past few hundreds of millions of years.

The transition zone

During the past few years the 1,800 or so miles of the mantle has been subdivided as more and more detailed information has been gleaned from earthquake-wave measurements.

The upper mantle is the region between the Moho and a depth of about 200 miles. The low-velocity layer is part of the upper mantle. Below 200 and stretching down to 600 miles is the 'transition layer', in which the seismic-wave velocity increases comparatively steeply (P waves, for example, from 5 to 7 miles a second). For the next 1,250 miles till the core is reached there is a gradual but steady increase in velocity (P increases to about 8·5 miles a second) in what is

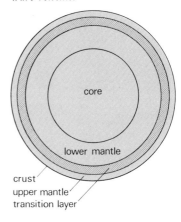

The transition zone and the other main subdivisions of the mantle, based on variations in P- and S-wave velocities

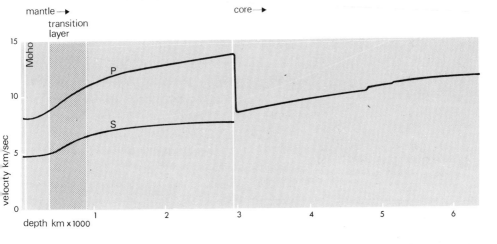

the lower mantle. Because the changes in velocity both in the upper mantle and in the transition zone are smooth, it is inferred that the mantle is all of one material. There is certainly no sharp discontinuity in seismic velocity and behaviour such as is observed at the Moho junction between crust and mantle, or at the mantle/core boundary. However, it is possible that the transition zone represents a gradual change of material, and not merely a gradation of physical properties. The elucidation of mantle structure provides plenty of interesting activity for several branches of geophysics. One line of attack is to work out the earth's heat-balance both now and in the past, but such calculations cannot approach precision until we know for certain the radioactive-heat contribution of the mantle.

There is another type of measurement which provides information about the mantle. Electric storms in the upper atmosphere cause currents to flow in the mantle. Brief storms lasting about a day affect the upper mantle only; but storms lasting several weeks can produce effects in the transition zone. By observing world-wide changes in the earth's magnetic field during these electric storms, it is possible to calculate the currents induced at various depths in the mantle, and from this to obtain the electrical conductivity of the rock. Electrical conductivity depends on temperature, and the magnetic measurements therefore make it possible to estimate the temperature gradient in the mantle independently of calculations concerned with heat-flow and radioactive-heat generation. The electrical conductivity helps directly in the heat-transfer calculations because it can be used to determine the absorption of radiation, which at the temperatures of a few thousand degrees centigrade in the mantle plays

Lightning strikes the conductor on top of the 1,250-foot Empire State Building in New York

an appreciable part in moving heat to the surface.

The slow movement in the mantle caused by changes of temperature due to heat from the liquid core and from radioactive decay, even though small compared with the volume of the mantle, are the prime-movers for the changes that occur in the earth's crustal rocks. We do not know exactly how or when or why changes occur in the mantle; we do not know which parts of the mantle can flow slowly because we are not certain about the rock temperature at various depths, and we do not know the physical properties of the mantle. It is probable, however, that the same basic chemical formulation of mantle material exists right through the mantle, but that, in the transition zone, changes of phase occur which give different physical properties to the rock, causing it to react differently under pressure and temperature. The keys to the problem of the mantle consist in the recovery of a sample of actual mantle rock, more widespread heat-flow measurements at the surface, more accurate seismic observations, and more detailed magnetic and electrical observations.

MAGNETISM AND THE CORE

Although it may be many years before a bore-hole is put down to reach the Moho and collect a virgin sample of mantle rock, it is inconceivable that the liquid core will ever be reached except indirectly through the geophysicist's seismic, gravity and magnetic experiments. The core is nearly 2,000 miles below the earth's surface, and will always remain something about which inspired speculation and confident deductions can be made, but which will never be able to be handled in substance. That a dense inner part of the earth exists there has been no question since the days of Newton. And the seismic evidence leaves little doubt that the outer part of the core at least is liquid.

It is popularly believed that the core consists of molten iron, and this is probably true. It must be admitted that this belief derives largely from the analogy with iron meteorites, but the calculated density of the core does support this view. However, the density does not appear to be exactly right for pure iron, or even for the iron-nickel mixture found in meteorites. The uncertainty lies in the effect of the great pressure—over a million times that exerted by the atmosphere—

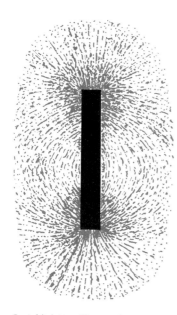

Sprinkled iron filings influenced by the magnetic field of an ordinary bar magnet reveal the magnetic lines of force, patterned much like those of the earth's own magnetic field

acting on the core and compressing its material. Until recently it has not been possible to simulate these pressures in the laboratory, but experiments involving the firing of iron bullets against a target are now in progress. Very high pressures are obtained, and the deformation of the iron can be observed. If the results are similar to those that would emerge with the application of a steady pressure, it appears that iron alone would give too large a density for that calculated for the core. It is quite easy to get over this hurdle, however, by assuming a small admixture of silicon in the core. Silicon is a common constituent of the earth, is lighter than iron, and would make it possible for the required reduction from a core of average density 7·9 to one of 6·9 to be achieved. This still does not rule out completely the possibility of a core of an initially lighter substance, either mantle rock or even hydrogen, which has been transformed by great pressure into a state where the atoms are abnormally compressed. Such a theory could account for the density of the core and, if true, would have an important bearing on accounts of the formation and history of the earth.

Whether the core is made of a molten iron alloy, or of some other substance in the metallic state, it is probably a good conductor of electricity and the source of the earth's magnetic field. Not all the planets have a magnetic field associated with them. The latest observations of Venus and Mars suggest that neither of these neighbours in the planetary family are so blessed, probably because the one does not rotate fast enough and the other has too small a liquid core. The magnetism associated with the earth provides a useful tool for investigating many terrestrial phenomena. The fossilized magnetic field buried in old layers of rock is, as we have seen, one of the indicators and plotters of the drift of the continents around the earth's surface. Measurement of present-day changes of the earth's magnetism also enables us to make sense of atmospheric phenomena and to find out more about the mantle.

The compass needle and its predecessor the lodestone were great aids to the discovery of the geographical features of the earth's surface, and observations of changes in the earth's magnetic field are available from Roman times. Today, what once appeared to be rather mundane collections of field-strength observations all over the oceans, are now proving vital to an understanding of the mechanisms of change in the earth's crust.

The core as a dynamo

The earth behaves as if it contains a gigantic bar magnet set in an approximately north-south direction. The familiar pattern that results from sprinkling iron filings on to a sheet of paper held over a magnet demonstrates very well how the influence of the earth's magnetic field extends above the earth's surface. A compass needle pivoted horizontally at the magnetic North Pole will point vertically downwards, while at the equator it will lie flat. Always it tends to align itself with the earth's magnetic lines of force, very similar in pattern to that assumed by the iron filings. This is to be expected, because the iron filings are behaving as hundreds of minute magnetic compass needles.

The magnetic North Pole does not coincide exactly with the true North Pole, which marks the earth's axis of rotation. The positions of the magnetic poles have in fact varied considerably during historical times. In Paris in 1580, for example, compasses pointed about 10° East of

Lodestone—a variety of the mineral magnetite—has a natural magnetic polarity. In the sixteenth century, when the magnetic polarity of the earth itself was first recognized, models of the earth were made by cutting small spheres from lodestone and locating and marking the magnetic poles

95

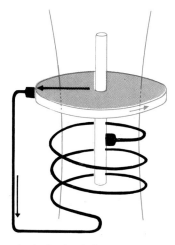

A cylindrical coil of wire carrying an electric current has a magnetic field like that of a bar magnet; and an electric current may be generated by rotating a copper disc over a coil, a in the simple disc dynamo below

true North, in 1820 nearly 24° West. The ten degrees or so difference between the compass needle's pointing and true North is always marked on charts, together with the amount that this difference changes each year, so it can be appreciated that the wandering of the magnetic field is readily observable and of practical importance. The strength of the earth's field also changes slightly with time, and these 'secular' variations of the magnetic field are probably associated with changes in the earth's liquid core.

The most reasonable explanation of the earth's magnetic field is that it is caused by a giant 'dynamo' which consists of the rotating, electrically conducting liquid iron core. The metallic conductor generates a current which must be enormous – about 10,000-million amperes. This tends to circulate around the axis of rotation of the earth, setting up a magnetic field in the same way that a cylindrical coil of wire carrying an electric current behaves like a bar magnet. There is a certain amount of doubt regarding the detail of this explanation. For example, it is not quite certain how the original magnetic field which interacts with the moving iron core was produced. However, once the 'dynamo' has started working, a second type of magnetic field probably arises. The liquid core moves relative to the mantle and in general gives the circulation necessary to provide the north-south magnetic field. In addition to this main movement, many subsidiary eddies would occur in the liquid core. Such eddies could cause the observed variations in the strength and direction of the earth's field. They could produce a coil-like magnetic field round the outer part of the core, and a little part of this field could leak out to make its presence felt at the earth's surface. Since the detailed form of the eddies varies slowly with time, the combined effect of their field and of the main axial rotational field is a slow wandering of the magnetic poles.

There are several regions of the world where variations in the field are more than usually intense. These regions are not associated with any particular surface features, except that perhaps the variations are less over the Pacific Ocean and higher than normal over Antarctica. The regions are the size of continents, but spread over land and ocean indiscriminately. The positions of the centres of greatest variation from the normal field slowly drift westward. Early explanations of these phenomena included the supposition of a series of small magnets placed around the junction between core and mantle, and it is probable from the time-scale of the effect that it has its origin in this part of the earth's interior. The concept of

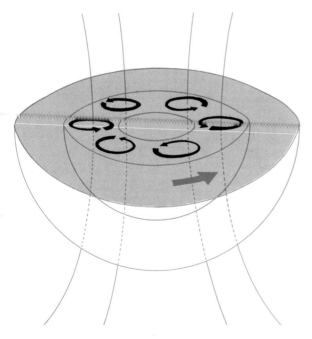

The shape of the earth's magnetic field suggests that circular electric currents are flowing in the earth's interior along planes roughly at right angles to the axis of rotation. It seems possible that these currents derive from local eddy currents produced in the liquid core by friction due to the earth's rotation

eddies in the liquid core is compatible with this thinking, and the westward drift may be, in a general sort of way, compared with the eastward drift of the cyclones and anticyclones in the atmosphere. Explanations of the earth's magnetic field based on the rotation of a liquid, conducting core, although far from complete, are, as Sir Edward Bullard put it, '. . . of the right degree of complexity to embrace the varied phenomena . . .' There is plenty of room in which the supporters of the theory can manoeuvre in order to accommodate new facts.

Magnetic field reversals

One complication which has already been added to the straightforward theory of the giant dynamo is the conception of two disc-shaped dynamos which are coupled together. Not only does this system take care of the earth's normal magnetic field, but it is also able to account for a field that can be reversed at intervals of the order of millions of years. A mechanism for this reversal of the earth's magnetic field on many occasions in the past is needed in order to explain three kinds of observation concerning the fossil magnetism in rocks. In the first place, there are several instances of successive flows of lava–in Iceland and other volcanic areas–which show adjacent rocks to be oppositely magnetized. At first it was believed that this phenomenon was due to some peculiar chemical property of the rock which allowed a reversal of the normal magnetic-field direction to be established. This does not appear, however, to fit all the known facts, and it is now almost certain that at given times the direction of the earth's magnetic field changes round, possibly instantaneously, but more probably in the course of thousands of years, so that what was magnetic

North becomes South and vice-versa. The period at which these lava rocks solidified can be dated, so that, for a few tens of millions of years at least, a history of when the poles were North or South has been delineated.

A similar history of reversals of the earth's magnetic field has been deduced from cores which have been collected from the floors of the deep oceans. The detail of the results obtained by examining ocean cores is greater than from the lava flows, since about an inch of sediment is deposited every 1,000 years, and now that a programme of collecting cores of ocean sediments down to thousands of feet below the sea-bed has been started, the earth's magnetic behaviour will be apparent back to about 120 million years. The results from cores fit very well with another line of evidence arising from oceanographic studies.

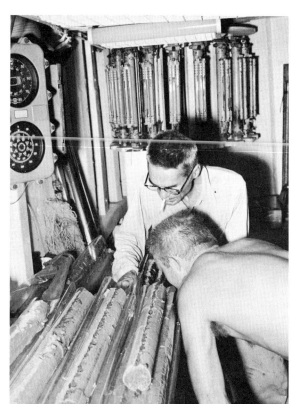

Geologists examining sedimentary cores taken from the sea-bed in the southwest Pacific

Right: readings of 'fossil' mag-netism (1) in volcanic rock associat-ed with mid-oceanic ridges reveals successive reversals of the earth's magnetic field. The symmetrical arrangement of the 'magnetic stripes' (2) to either side of the range, sug-gesting that fresh lava deposits not only overlie older deposits – as shown by taking core samples (3) – but also push them steadily outwards away from the ridge, is most convincing evidence of a mechanism for con-tinental drift

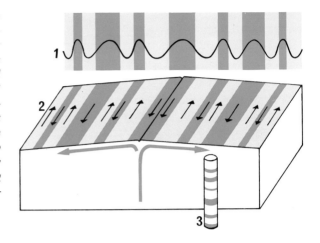

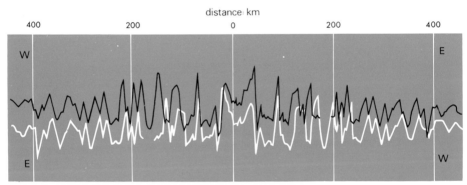

A demonstration of the symmetry of an actual magnetic trace over a mid-oceanic ridge

Magnetic measurements over the deep oceans show a regular pattern of magnetic abnormalities, and these are probably due to lava flows which have burst out at intervals in the past. When the lava solidifies on the sea-bed, and cools below 600°C., it acquires a magnetic field in the direc-tion of the earth's field prevailing at that instant. The magnetism of successive lava flows on the ocean-bed may therefore be normal or reversed. If the ocean-floor moves, spreading outwards from a central ridge which is a sporadic supplier of volcanic lava, then the normal and reversed magnetized lava will be spread out like the stripes of a zebra across the ocean-floor. This appears to be the case since the pattern of magnetic plus and minus is symmetrical about the mid-ocean axis.

There is, then, solid modern evidence that magnetic-field reversals do occur, and these reversals fit in very nicely with the moving-sea-floor theory, which in turn simplifies many other facts concerning the earth's surface.

An examination of the minute fossil remains of small sea plants and animals which are embedded in the cores from the sea-floor show some interesting correlations with the reversals of magnetic field. At some reversals it has been noted that certain species of *radiolaria* become extinct. It has been suggested that, during the period in which the change-over from North to South takes place, there is a time of zero field strength which allows an extra supply of cosmic rays from

A paleontologist studies the fossil remains of marine life contained in core samples

the sun, together with particles trapped in the outer atmosphere radiation belts, to strike the earth. Bombardment by these high-energy particles could possibly cause extinction of a species of animal or plant, or it could be the start of a new species formed by mutation. Unfortunately this interesting speculation is unlikely to be true because of the shielding of the earth by its atmosphere. However, there is another line of evidence which has a bearing on the matter. In the deep sea cores there is an extra abundance of tektites around the intervals of magnetic field reversal. Tektites are fragments of melted rock produced when meteorites strike the earth, and it has been proposed that a big meteorite impact provides the hammer blow that makes the earth's core dynamo reverse and change the direction of the magnetic field.

Barringer's Crater in Arizona. Nearly a mile in diameter, it was produced about 20,000 years ago by an iron-nickel meteorite weighing many thousands of tons

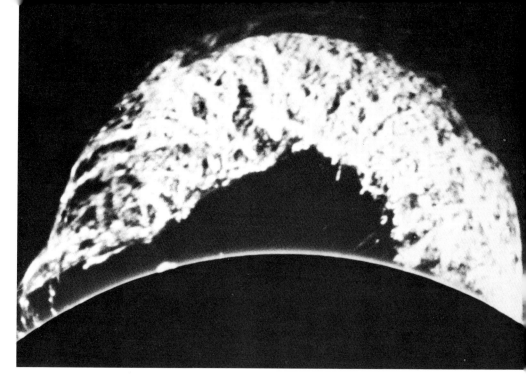

Effects of the 'solar wind'

Part of the sun's output of energy reaches the neighbourhood of the earth, and part of it penetrates through the earth's atmosphere to reach the surface in the form of sunlight: part is stopped by the atmosphere and the region of space above it. It is in this region that the electrically-charged hydrogen atoms thrown out by disturbances on the sun, what is often called the 'solar wind', are trapped.

The earth is surrounded by a girdle-like region starting a few hundred miles above the surface and extending 36,000 miles into space. The girdle is at its thickest and highest over the equator and tails away towards the poles, dipping down towards the atmosphere. At first there appeared to be two separate layers or belts of particles with a gap between them; now it appears more likely that there is only one, whose position and particle population change with time.

A soaring arch of flaming hydrogen, already towering more than 200,000 miles above the sun's surface, streaming out into space

103

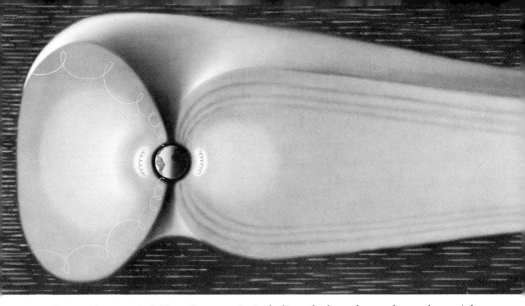

The earth's magnetic field as distorted by the 'wind' of radiant energy issuing from the sun. The zones of intense Van Allen-belt radiation are indicated by the corkscrew paths described by charged atomic particles along the magnetic lines of force

It is believed that these charged particles are trapped in the magnetic field of the earth. They follow a corkscrew or helical path in the magnetic field, moving from pole to pole along the magnetic lines of force. As one of the particles moves towards a pole it finds a steadily increasing magnetic field which gradually reduces the pitch of the helix, until the particle is eventually moving back towards the equator.

Whether the magnetic field helps to protect the earth from outer space bombardment by deflection of the 'solar wind' particles which stream out from the sun or not, there is certainly a strong interaction between the ionized layers of the upper atmosphere and the earth's magnetism. The layers of the atmosphere about 100 miles up are important because, since they contain ionized particles and are therefore conducting, they reflect radio waves, and also behave in a peculiar fashion towards the radiation that is sent out by the sun.

The radiation belt round the earth provides a partial explanation for the aurora, the patterns of brilliant red, green and blue flames, curtains, rays and arcs seen in the polar sky during periods of solar activity. Study of the aurora during the

International Geophysical Year (1957-8) showed that displays occurred simultaneously across the entire night sky in northern and southern hemispheres. The familiar glows occur at heights of 60 to 100 miles above the surface in the upper layers of the atmosphere, and the flickering light is produced in much the same way as the red light of a neon sign–by the excitation of the atoms in a rarefied gas. Odd forms of aurora may be as high as 600 miles.

It now appears that the excitation of the atoms of oxygen and nitrogen in the upper atmosphere is due to collision with charged hydrogen atoms from the sun. These charged particles are probably spilled out of the Van Allen radiation belt when a powerful outburst from the sun distorts the magnetic field. The particles then corkscrew down into the atmosphere without having reached a magnetic field strong enough to turn them back towards the equator. In fact, the radiation belt appears to behave as a kind of gas-bag. The solar wind fills the bag in great gusts so that from time to time it overflows, creating the aurora.

An auroral display recently observed by Japanese scientists at a research station in Antarctica

The atmosphere

The earth's surface is completely immersed in a gaseous atmosphere, held by gravitational forces. The composition of the atmosphere varies with altitude. It appears that from 1,500 to 6,000 miles above the surface hydrogen is the main element present, while helium occupies the zone from 600 to 1,500 miles altitude. From 72 to 600 miles the atmosphere is mostly oxygen, with some nitrogen in the form of nitrous oxide. Below 72 miles the atmosphere gradually assumes the 78 per cent nitrogen, 21 per cent oxygen mixture that we breathe on earth. The odd one per cent is made up mainly of argon with traces of carbon dioxide, neon, helium, methane, krypton, nitrous oxide, hydrogen, ozone and xenon.

The atmosphere exerts a pressure of 14·7 pounds per square inch at the earth's surface and it is concentrated close to the earth by the earth's gravitational pull. At a height of 70 miles the pressure is only two-millionths of a pound per square inch.

In the upper tenuous layers of the atmosphere, the energetic X-ray and ultra-violet radiation from the sun is absorbed by the atoms and molecules. The result is that electrons are stripped from the neutral atoms, and so, in these regions, the atmosphere contains large numbers of charged particles or ions.

The ionosphere is responsible for the daily variations in the earth's magnetic field, which are caused by powerful currents flowing through it. These currents are particularly strong when the sun is disturbed and is emitting a greater quantity of X-rays than usual. The result is a 'magnetic storm' in which the earth's magnetic field is disturbed. At these times radio communications via the ionosphere are also upset. Sometimes communication becomes impossible; at others, radio

Astronaut Edward White 'walks' in space during the Gemini-4 *flight in 1965, the centrifugal effect of his rapid orbital motion counter-balancing the pull of the earth's gravity. There is no oxygen in the extremely rarefied atmosphere at this altitude, and he has to breathe through the 25-foot, gold-taped 'umbilical' tube. An emergency oxygen pack is strapped to his chest*

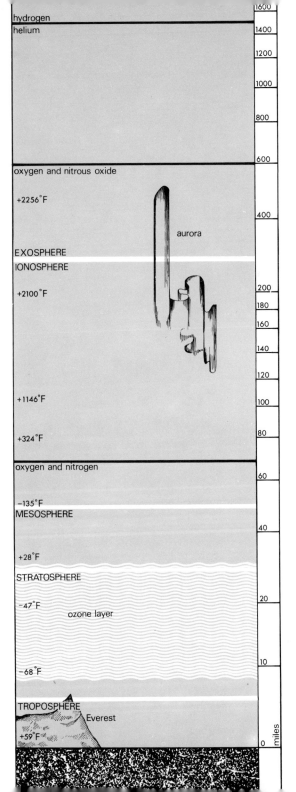

Profile of the atmosphere (on a diminishing vertical scale). Atmospheric pressure rapidly decreases as altitude increases: although the earth's gaseous envelope extends to an altitude of over a thousand miles, nine-tenths of its 4,000-million tons' content lies within 20 miles of the surface. The chief constituents are the gases oxygen and nitrogen, the abundance of the former—and to some extent the latter—due to the respiration of living organisms. Auroral displays occur in the ionosphere, which also acts as a reflector of radio signals. Meteors, travelling at up to 15 miles a second, generally burn out in or above the stratosphere. The atmosphere also protects living things from bombardment by lethal solar radiation

waves of such high frequency that they are not normally reflected by the ionosphere are returned to earth. This is the explanation of the occasional reports that television signals (which have frequencies too high to be reflected by the ionosphere under normal conditions, and therefore cannot be received beyond 'line of sight') have been received in other continents without the mediation of a relay satellite.

Motion in the core

A dynamo needs an engine to keep it turning. Three possible sources of power have been suggested to keep the liquid iron rotating and swirling sufficiently to provide the electric current needed to maintain the earth's magnetic field. The inner core of the earth may still be enlarging and the heat given out in the change from liquid to solid could provide the energy to boil up the liquid in the core. Another way in which energy could be transferred to the core is by the precessional motion of the earth in its orbit. Any unsteadiness in the motion of the earth could impart a rotary action by friction between the mantle and the core. The stirring of the core may, on the other hand, be the result of radioactive heating, perhaps produced by promontories of mantle protruding into the core, but more probably by the solid inner core itself. It is almost certain, from the earthquake-wave evidence, that a solid inner core exists, but its properties are even more conjectural than those of the other parts of the earth's interior. In general, it may be assumed that the inner core is much denser than its liquid surround, and it could conceivably contain some uranium which would make it a heat source.

As the earth cooled and solidified, water which had been uniformly distributed in the molten rock was extruded. Since the earth at this time was very hot, the water would have been in the form of steam, and it was only after subsequent cooling that a long period of condensation took place to form the oceans. It may sound odd for water to be associated with molten rock, but it has been found experimentally that at high temperatures and pressures water and silicates are miscible in all proportions, and if all the water on the earth were changed to steam it would produce suitable conditions for mixing with the earth's mantle. The extrusion of water during solidification, and the cooling necessary to allow the steam to condense took place very quickly on the geological time-scale. We can calculate what the loss of heat would be from a body that was initially at the temperature of molten rock, about 1,500°C. From the rate of loss of heat we find that the mantle would solidify in about 10,000 years; and in say 15,000 years the cooling would have continued sufficiently for the water to condense. The oceans, then, have been a part of the earth since the earliest times.

Man explores the hydrosphere. The lobster-like bow of the Aluminaut— *an aluminium submarine designed to operate at depths of up to three miles —looms myopically through the cloudy water. About 60 per cent of the world's ocean-floor is accessible to its crew*

If we subscribe to the theory that Mars and the moon derived from the earth, the original ocean would have occupied the two-thirds of the earth's surface centred on the position of today's Pacific Ocean. The land would have been a solid mass opposite to this ocean, probably with rather ragged edges, and perhaps with a few outliers of crustal material which had spilled back during the enormous break-up as Mars departed. It is probable that the land mass remained in one piece for thousands of millions of years, because the geological evidence concerned with continental drift suggests two major movements, that of India from Africa, and that of the Americas from Africa and Europe, as taking place within the last few hundred million years.

The large land mass would have been subjected to buckling and tilting, in a manner similar to that which affects the continents today. Shallow continental fringes would appear, and folding of the land would produce basins which would pull the rivers towards them and attract sediments from the elevated parts of the continent. Since water was present on the earth from the earliest days, the processes of erosion and the formation of new layers of rock have taken place for virtually the whole duration of the earth's existence. With only one land mass the coastline would be much shorter than it is today, so that formation of sedimentary rocks would be slow at the beginning, but would accelerate as the original land mass broke up. Furthermore, since sedimentary rocks are often softer and more readily attacked by ice and water, the rate of production of new sediments would increase with time. We live in a period of near maximum sediment formation. Local increases may have taken place just after periods of mountain building, because land of

The fertile Nile delta, formed of silt swept down to the Mediterranean from the Ethiopian Highlands. (Cairo is at the apex of the delta; in the background are the Suez Canal and the Siniai Peninsula)

high elevation is more rapidly eroded than low-lying plains, because of ice formation and faster-moving rivers.

The size of the land portion of the earth may have increased due to spreading of sediment beyond the original continental boundaries, but seismic observations suggest that the greater part of the sediments were deposited in shallow water on the continental shelves, which are an integral part of the land mass. Some increase may also have taken place due to a pushing sideways of the land in order to accommodate the intrusions of volcanic material that have forced their way out of the underlying mantle, in much the same way as Iceland has expanded to provide room for the

113

volcanic dykes with which it is riddled. However, the land, even with its continental shelves, occupies less than one-third of the earth's surface; the other two-thirds is covered by water which is on average about three miles deep. To some marine geologists the sea-floor is typical of the earth's surface, the continental blocks exceptional.

Charting the sea-bed

The sea, contrary to ideas prevailing during the last century, is neither uniformly deep nor bottomless. The floor of the Pacific, as we know it, is becoming less flat year by year. This is not so much due to the inconstancy of nature as to the energy with which the problem of deep-ocean sounding is being approached. Every oceanographic expedition now makes routine soundings while voyaging from one experimental site to the next, and where possible the route is chosen to cover hitherto uncharted parts of the ocean. This is not difficult, because only about 10 per cent of the Pacific has so far been examined in sufficient detail to ensure that no large underwater features have been missed. Even today, it is quite normal to find a major submerged mountain on every voyage. Recently an estimate was made of the total number of islands and atolls, which can be readily counted, and major undersea features, detectable only by echo-sounder. It is probable that somewhere between about 5,000 and 10,000 of these 'pimples' exist in the Pacific. This corresponds to about one major feature for every hundred-mile-sided square of ocean bottom. Only about 800 of these submarine features have so far been discovered, but the total number may be estimated by assuming that the concentration of features is much the same in the uncharted 90 per cent of the Pacific. A similar figure is obtained by comparing the total length of ships' tracks which have been sounded with the observed average value for the number of submerged features per thousand miles; and yet a third similar figure is obtained by taking a well-explored area and extrapolating over the whole Pacific. It is possible, of course, that these figures are over-estimates because the visible islands often form a line like the Hawaiian chain of islands, and this may lead to a false value for the concentration of submerged features in other parts of the ocean. The only sure way to find out the extent of the underwater features of the Pacific is to make a complete chart of the sea-bed, and oceanographers are pressing on with this work. Progress is slow because the only really reliable results come from research expeditions, naval survey ships and from cable-laying vessels. Passenger and cargo ships are normally fitted with echo-sounders that have a depth limit of only a few hundred fathoms.

The average depth of the oceans is about 14,000 feet, but this includes the shallow areas around islands and undersea mountains. There are many deep basins whose depth is 17,000 to 18,000 feet, and these can be regarded as the true floor of the oceans. There are deeper places, whose special geological significance will one day be elucidated, but these, together with the pinnacles and ridges which protrude from the ocean-floor, and about which a great deal is already known, are exceptional modifications of a mainly uniform layering of rock in the earth's crust.

The deep basins are extraordinarily flat-bottomed. It is a common experience, when watching the echo-sounder, for several hours to pass with virtually no change in depth recorded. High-precision records of flat basins in the Atlantic show that the depth is constant for miles

Abyssal Plain

on end to within a fathom; in fact, contours at one-fathom intervals have been drawn of basins nearly three-thousand fathoms deep. The basins are shown to slope very gently from the edges towards the centre.

These basins are not the primeval ocean-floor, because samples of the bottom are found to consist of soft sediment. Moreover, the flat part is generally bordered by a more rugged portion of sea-bed and the junction of the two types of topography is marked by a distinct change in slope. The seismic measurements show that the sediment thickness in the flat areas varies considerably, so that it is fairly clear that they are ponds of sediment giving an artificially flat appearance to the original rugged form of the ocean-floor. There may of course be places where the original floor was flat and in these the sediment blanket has merely made a faithful reproduction of what is underneath. Detailed sounding over the boundaries of the flat basins and careful checks of adjacent basins show beyond doubt that they are caused by the flow of fluid material downhill from shallow to deeper water. If neighbouring basins are discovered with slightly different levels, a thorough search will always reveal a spill-point where the dammed-up sediment from the upper basin has poured over to fill up the lower one.

Undersea mountains

There are some conspicuous flat areas in the Pacific that have different characteristics from the sediment basins. These are generally found to be

Atlantic   Atlantis
Seamount   Azores   Josephine Gettysburg
Seamount   Seamount   Gibraltar

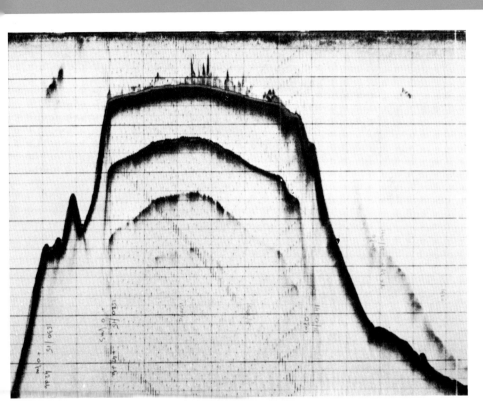

Above: an echo-sounding trace of the Gettysburg sea-mount in the Atlantic. From its summit – 700 feet below the surface – its steep slopes fall away to a depth of over 5,000 feet. Left: silt on the ocean bottom 13,000 feet down off Cape Horn.

centred on an island or a similar submerged feature. They have been termed archipelagic aprons, because they are probably the result of volcanic eruptions that have gradually spread from a long crack in the ocean-floor rather than from a volcanic cone, but the result is much the same, except that the symmetry of the gentle slopes is altered. These flat areas around volcanoes might conceivably have been produced by the ash sent out in enormous quantity during eruptions. But calculation shows that the quantity of ash likely to be expelled is inadequate to account for the large area of the archipelagic aprons.

Volcanic activity is certainly a powerful force in altering the appearance of the earth's surface. In the Pacific Ocean there are hundreds of islands and atolls which are all formed by eruptions which have started from the sea-bed and gradually piled up solid material. In Hawaii the great peak of Mauna Loa rises to a height of 14,000 feet above sea-level, and it is supported by more than two miles of submerged trunk. If only the sea could be drained away, the view from Mauna Loa would out-rival any Japanese print of beautiful, symmetrical volcanic peaks. Rising with graceful curves from a vast flat ocean-floor, the smooth slopes of the mountains would be unspoilt by the eroding action of glaciers and rivers. Some of the peaks would be like crowns, their tops encircled by a regular rim of coral rock, and most of these would be at exactly the same height, for they are the atolls, which rise only a few feet above sea-level. There would be many other flat-topped peaks of lesser height, looking as if some fickle giant had arbitrarily lopped off the peaks of volcanoes to provide seats and tables. Interspersed with these would be regular cones of all sizes and ages—some smoking as a sign of continuing activity. For many years these lovely volcanic features of the Pacific have aroused speculation, especially the truncated cones, which are unfamiliar on land, but the combination of seismic and echo-sounder measurements has lately resulted in an unravelling of the mystery, so that now a single mechanism can explain them all.

However, the sea-bed features do not consist entirely of isolated peaks or groups of peaks growing from a flat plain. The sea-floor itself is heavily corrugated by the same compressional forces that have pushed up the mountain ranges on the continents. Sometimes the underwater folds are large enough to be designated mountain ranges themselves. In the Pacific, volcanic islands often lie in regular lines, and an examination of the chart shows that the islands have grown up on a gentle rise of several thousand feet above the normal deep-sea floor. Then there are great topographical features like the Mid-Atlantic Ridge. It is as though someone had attempted to build a wall to separate the two Atlantic shore lines. The wall is not complete, since above most parts of the Ridge there is a 1,500-fathom cover of water. But pictured from below it is a gigantic mountain range, reaching up to about 10,000 feet from the ocean-bed for most of its length. In many parts it is marked by volcanic islands, such as the Azores, or by shallows, such as the isolated St Paul's Rocks near the equator, but these are probably secondary features. The important characteristic of the Mid-Atlantic Ridge is the way it follows a median line between the land on either side of the Atlantic, and this could be due to the symmetrical interplay of the unexplained forces that buckle the earth's crust to form mountains, or it could be a vestigial consequence of the drifting apart of the east and west land masses. The latest magnetic evidence

A new volcanic island, Ilha Nova, breaks the surface near the island of Fayal, in the Azores, on 27 September 1957

suggests that the Ridge is a constant source of new rock which has the effect of gradually driving the Atlantic's eastern and western shores farther and farther apart.

Ridges and trenches

There are in the oceans features indicating that parts of the crust have been stretched. Down the middle of the Mid-Atlantic Ridge there is a parallel-sided valley which has every appearance of a tear in the ocean-floor. Similar rift-valleys, as they are called, exist in Africa, and the Red Sea itself has been formed by the development of a similar feature between Arabia and Egypt. The detailed surveys that are now being made by echo-sounder show that this kind of fault in the earth's crust is comparatively common in the Pacific and the Indian Ocean, and it is in the oceans that the meaning of rift-valleys in terms of the earth's structural history will probably be elucidated, because in the oceans the evidence has not been destroyed by weathering and erosion.

The Mid-Atlantic Ridge is not the only under-sea mountain range, but is one example of a world-wide system of mid-ocean ridges that extends round the southern end of Africa across the Indian Ocean and into the Pacific, eventually reaching the California coast, and bringing with it earth movements of the kind that wrecked San Francisco at the turn of the century.

The Suez region and the Gulf of Suez, at the head of the Red Sea, photographed from Gemini 5

Members of the civilian scientific staff aboard H.M.S. Challenger *during the pioneer oceanographic expedition of 1872–6*

Valleys on a gigantic scale have been revealed by soundings in the deep parts of the oceans. In the last century the Challenger Expedition found one isolated depth of 27,000 feet in the Pacific. This was a mile and a half deeper than the usual value of about three miles, Such features, known as the deep trenches, extend for hundreds of miles along the Pacific as fifty-mile-wide valleys with depths approaching six miles. In these trenches are to be found all the deepest parts of the ocean, but although there are 'record' depths just as there are largest and smallest of most things on earth, the interesting fact from the geological point of view is that many of the trenches are close to five and a half miles deep for the greater part of their length. It is as if there is a limit to the maximum depth that is possible, and that all trenches approach this limit. There are some, of course, such as that running in an east-west arc south of the Aleutian Islands, where a depth of just over four miles is reached, but here there are indications of a general uplift of the whole sea-floor, and it is of course possible that some filling of the trench by sediment has taken place. The deeper trenches run southward to the east of Japan and the Marianas Islands before swinging round to point in an east-west direction towards the Palau Islands. Another well-known trench runs along the eastern side of the Philippine Islands. To the north-east of New Zealand are the Kermadec and Tonga trenches. It is probable that these deep trenches are the ocean counterparts of the deep basins of deposition that can be seen on the continents, in the Persian Gulf area, for example.

The sea-bed does not suffer the ravages of ice and wind and moving water which erode the land. But while the original features of the ocean floor are preserved, they are in many places buried by sediments. Fine particles, which take so long

Map of the world's principal mid-oceanic ridge and trench systems

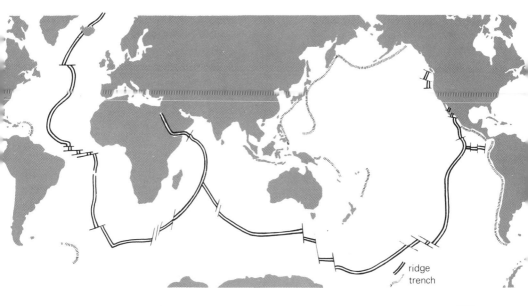

ridge
trench

to settle that they are carried past the main depositional areas of the continental shelves, are augmented by a fine rain of cosmic dust from outer space and by the skeletons and shells of sea animals to produce a few thousand feet of soft clay over the greater part of the sea-floor. However, not all the sediment is fine grained, for stones and boulders are sometimes dredged from the deepest parts of the oceans. These have been rafted from the continents by icebergs, which drop their cargo when they melt.

Turbidity currents

A further source of supply of sea-bed sediment from the continents is provided by another fascinating mechanism. Although the floor of the deep oceans is as black as night and is normally as quiet as a few unusual fishes and burrowing holothurians will allow, every now and then a rushing torrent sweeps down the slopes of the continental shelf to disturb the sediments much more drastically than could any animals or gentle

Creatures of the deep. Below left: a tripod fish hops along the sea-bed on stilt-like fins. Right: a sea spider— 28 inches across—three brittlestars, and numerous tracks, at a depth of 6,00 feet, off Cape Cod

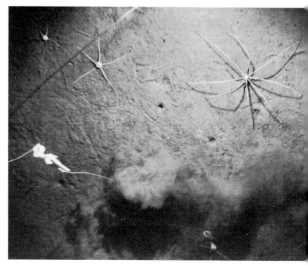

water movement. These are the turbidity currents, and they probably do more to mix up the sediments of the oceans than any other process. They are formed by a suspension of mud in water, and this mixture, being heavier than the plain water, tends to sink. If the sea-bed is sloping, as it is on the continental shelf, the mud-and-water mixture starts to flow downhill, just like a river. The slopes are steep and long, and the mud and water gradually gathers speed until it is moving as fast as an express train. Once started in this way, the very force of the current scours up fresh bottom material to augment its initial volume, and the torrent careers downwards until it comes to the flat plains of the deep ocean, where its momentum allows it to gouge out a river-bed in the sediment that has already collected there.

Now, it may seem strange that a stream of mud and water can move through water with the speed of an express train. In fact, when the turbidity current was first mooted it was greeted with scepticism by many geologists. It becomes a little

Above left: a turbidity current in miniature: a 30-foot underwater 'sandfall' in the Cape San Lucas submarine canyon off California. Right: an alpine avalanche suggests something of the scale of a turbidity current

easier to visualize if it is compared with avalanches in snow fields. In some avalanches one body of snow slides comparatively slowly over rock, or over more snow, in the same way that snow slides off a warm roof, but there are times when the snow and air form a turbulent mixture which races down the mountainside at speeds of the order of hundreds of miles an hour. Then again, there are the katabatic winds which flow at up to a hundred miles an hour down mountainsides in some parts of the world. These winds are merely the result of a cold, and therefore heavy, layer of air sliding in turbulent fashion below the normal warm air. It is easy to see that high speeds are possible if once it is admitted that the resistance to motion is small. Sometimes a mixture of ash and hot gases from a volcano forms a layer that is heavier than the surrounding air; instead of sliding gently down the slopes of the mountain the mixture rushes down at great speed to catch its victims unawares, as in the suffocating holocaust of Mount Pelée. Mathematical calculations show that a mud suspension, provided it moves in a turbulent fashion, should be able to flow in flat streams about ten feet thick with surprisingly little friction. This theoretical work is supported by model experiments which demonstrate the way in which turbidity currents maintain their identity even though they are flowing through water which would be expected at first sight to oppose and break up the forward movement. No one has actually seen a large-scale turbidity current, so that the fact that models and mathematics show them to be possible does not mean that they do play any part in the formation of the deep oceans. However, there are several pieces of experimental evidence which can be readily accounted for if turbidity currents are accepted.

Many cores taken from the flat sea-bed of the Atlantic show not just plain clay, but alternating bands of sand and silt, together with fossils similar to those found in shallow-water animals. It is possible that some movement from shallow to deep water could take place by the slumping of great portions of sediment down the continental slope, and such slumping undoubtedly does take place. It does not explain, however, the long distance of travel that is necessary to account for the presence of some sand and shallow-water fossils far out in the almost flat part of the deep ocean. And it does not explain the details of the bedding and grading of sand grains which are observed in the deep-sea cores, and which fit the turbidity-current theory very nicely.

Although the laying of the Atlantic cable in the nineteenth century was one of the main reasons for first undertaking the study of the sea-bed, it was not until comparatively recently that modern

A street scene in Saint-Pierre, Martinique, after the devastating eruption of Mount Pelée in 1902

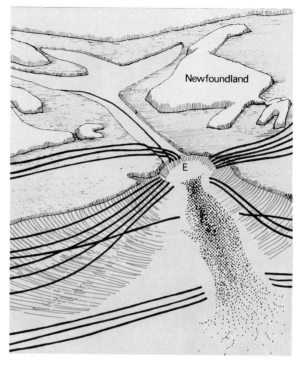

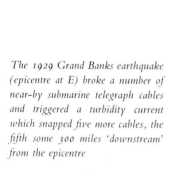

The 1929 Grand Banks earthquake (epicentre at E) broke a number of near-by submarine telegraph cables and triggered a turbidity current which snapped five more cables, the fifth some 300 miles 'downstream' from the epicentre

oceanographers and cable layers found that they had between them a fascinating set of experimental facts relating to turbidity currents. Cable-breaks have long been associated with earthquakes, but it was always considered strange that, when several cables were broken by an earthquake, they did not break simultaneously. The times of failure were usually recorded accurately since the cables were in use. It is possible that the earthquake loosened a large mass of sediment, which slumped on to the cables, but large masses of sediment do not travel very far—unless, that is, they form a turbidity current. Turbidity currents could travel down the continental slope, cutting all cables in their path. The time-sequences of cable-breaks can in fact be accounted for by a turbidity current, which always moves downhill, as one would expect, and travels at a speed of about 50 miles per hour on the 1-in-10 slopes, and at a slower speed of about 12 miles per hour when the flatter part of the ocean-floor is reached. Thus, not only can the cable-breaks be plausibly explained, but in addition the times and locations of the breaks can give a measure of the speed of travel of the currents.

Layer 2

Seismic measurements show that there are several thousand feet of a harder material beneath the sediments before the hard basalt, which is generally supposed to be the original rock floor of the oceans, is reached. This intermediate layer, or 'Layer 2', as it is commonly called, has not yet been identified with any particular rock type. It is probable that it consists of different material in different parts of the sea-floor. Near volcanic islands Layer 2 is almost certainly lava which has spread over the sea-floor and subsequently been covered by soft sediment. However, Layer 2 is observed in the flat parts of the ocean-floor well away from any island or sea-mount which could have provided lava. It is possible that splits in the sea-floor have opened up to supply volcanic material, but a more likely explanation is that here Layer 2 consists of a super-hardened layer of sediment. There are two ways in which the hardening could have occurred. At some period in the earth's history, perhaps in Cretaceous times, there might have been an enormous expansion in the numbers of marine animals. The debris from animal corpses would have carried quantities of calcium-carbonate to the sea-floor and this would have formed a hard limestone. Layer 2 would then consist of a thin limestone layer, and would have beneath it a further few thousand feet of soft

Section through the sea-bed, showing the location of Layer 2

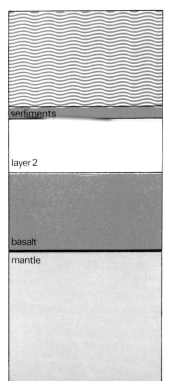

sediment before the original rock floor of the ocean is reached. Another possibility is that a heating up of the ocean-floor occurred and baked the soft clay sediment into hard shale.

One day, bore-holes will be drilled through the soft sediment into Layer 2. It is important to find out what Layer 2 is because if it forms part of the secondary material that has been deposited on the sea-bed the total sediment thickness is much greater than if Layer 2 is an outpouring of volcanic lava. Attempts have been made to determine the ages of ocean basins by assuming a steady rate of sediment deposition, but such calculations are meaningless if we do not know the true thickness of sediments. If we favour continental drift, the Atlantic Ocean is very young compared with the Pacific. Yet Layer 2, together with the sediment, is much the same thickness in both oceans. This could be partly accounted for by the closer source of supply in the Atlantic, which was in its earlier days a narrow sea fed by material from land masses to the east and to the west. On the other hand, if the sea-floor is in constant motion due to convection currents, both ocean-floors would be comparatively recent. More facts are needed and perhaps the core samples now being gathered by the United States Deep-Sea Drilling Project's survey vessel *Glomar Challenger* will supply them.

Sea-floor spreading

The sinking of volcanic islands to form coral atolls is another example of the plasticity of the mantle, which allows the continental blocks to find their own equilibrium level, as if they were floating icebergs. In addition to the up and down movements, and the tiltings that have taken place in the past, there are signs on the sea-bed of large sideways movements of the earth's crust.

Part of the old opposition to Wegener's original theory of continental drift was due to the large horizontal movements that were needed. Today more and more examples of very large horizontal tears in the earth's crust are being found. Magnetic measurements over a large part of the eastern Pacific show a pattern of anomalies which runs regularly north and south. Along at least two east-west lines in the area, there are horizontal displacements of the vertical pattern of anomalies by several hundred miles, indicating east-west horizontal movements associated with two large fault zones. In the same area, study of the well-known San Andreas fault in California shows that over millions of years enormous movements have taken place. In Chile, recent disastrous earthquakes caused visible horizontal movements of many feet which, repeated over millions of years, would add up to hundreds of miles.

The details of the emerging pattern of magnetic observations in the oceans have been elegantly fitted by F. J. Vine and D. Matthews to the theory of a spreading of the ocean-floor from a central ridge which is the seat of an upwelling convection current in the mantle. The earth's magnetic field reverses periodically, and since the molten rock which is extruded to form fresh ocean-floor takes on the magnetic field direction existing at the time of cooling, the spreading sea-floor will consist of a series of magnetic stripes. The significant point of the observations is that the pattern of stripes is symmetrical about the centre line, as one would expect on the theory of a continuously moving ocean-floor.

Another type of geophysical measurement in the oceans has provided further evidence in favour of the theory of continental drift. The gravitational attraction of the earth varies by a few

Top: the track followed by the magnetic survey vessel that discovered two major fault zones on the Pioneer Ridge in the eastern Pacific. Bottom: magnetic traces recorded along segments A and B. If B is moved 138 miles to the west, the traces match perfectly

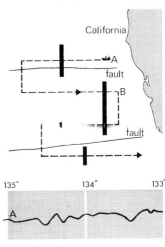

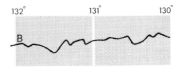

parts in a million, depending on the details of the rock structure beneath the point of observation. A definite pattern of change is observed, for example, when crossing from continent to deep ocean across the continental slope. A similar pattern was found in readings over the rim of the plateau in the Indian Ocean on which the Seychelles Islands lie. The Seychelles have always been a geological anomaly in that large parts of the main islands are composed of granite, rather than the normal volcanic material which forms most oceanic islands. The gravity results, confirmed later by seismic determinations of crustal thickness suggested that the Seychelles are continental rather than oceanic in their geological structure. This is what would be expected if southern India drifted away from southern Africa and left a fragment of 'micro-continent' half way along the line.

Slight variations in gravity readings at the earth's surface may roughly indicate the depths of heavy rock formations and whether folding or faulting has occurred. Below left: lowering a gravity meter at sea. Right: a skin diver examines the position of another gravity meter on the sea-bed off Abu Dhabi in the Persian Gulf

There are probably many more such micro-continents in the oceans over which drift has taken place.

An interesting part of the ocean, the investigation of which has further strengthened the theory of continental drift, is the Mediterranean Sea. Although the Mediterranean is not a typical ocean now, it probably started life as a true deep ocean separating the continents of Europe and Africa. These continents were gradually worn down by the normal processes of erosion, and the debris was carried out to sea and dumped on the continental shelves in the usual way. The original ocean, being narrow, eventually filled up altogether. It only required a comparatively small vertical movement to transform the basin into the centre of a continent stretching from England to the Sahara. The exact reason for these vertical movements is not known, but the evidence of many large thicknesses of rock above sea-level shows that they must take place frequently in the course of geological history.

Examinations of the rocks indicates that the next step in the evolution of the Mediterranean

An astronaut's panoramic view of the western Mediterranean. The Straits of Gibraltar are in the foreground, with Spain to the left and Morocco to the right

was for the centre of the area again to become a sea. This happened in Middle Triassic times – about 170-million years ago – and it did so because the European and African continents moved apart. It is possible that the filling up and splitting apart process was repeated a second time about 30-million years ago, and the present sea-bed, which reaches depths about half those of the major oceans, is the result of the subsidence of the second period of land or shallow sea in the area. The floor of the Mediterranean is therefore much more complicated in structure than those of the other oceans, but when the relevant geological details have been discovered, they will no doubt be explained by the varying pressures caused by the relative movements of the African and European blocks.

A glance at the map will show a very twisted pattern of land joining North and South America. This area, if the theory of continental drift is accepted, has undergone very violent movements, and it is not surprising that the structure of the sea-bed is complicated. At first it was believed that the Caribbean Sea was a very old ocean basin sealed off from the Atlantic. However, structures which may be salt domes have been located by geophysical measurements in the Sigsbee Deep. Salt means shallow-water evaporation, and it now appears possible that this part of the deep-sea bed has been forced down from sea-level. If this is true it tends to contradict the concept of permanent ocean basins and permanent continental blocks. The Caribbean is, however, only a very small part of the ocean and it is in a place where exceptional activity would have been expected during the movement of the Americas to produce the Atlantic. In general the continents may be tilted or warped to form shallow shelf seas, but it is improbable that large continental blocks founder to form large areas of ocean.

The JOIDES operation

More experimental results are needed to find out what has happened in the past to produce the geological features of the oceans. One of the more interesting projects in progress is the Joint Oceanographic Institutes Deep-Earth Sampling, or JOIDES, programme, which provides for a series of bore-holes drilled from a surface ship into the sea-floor. The operation is technically similar to the Mohole, by which it was hoped to penetrate the crust where it was thinnest under the deep oceans in order to sample the mantle. The JOIDES bore-holes penetrate through the soft sediment which covers the sea-floor, and sample Layer 2. The penetration of Layer 2 will depend on how long the drill-bit lasts, since there is no facility for re-entering the bore-hole in the sea-bed three miles below the sea-surface. The JOIDES holes should satisfy curiosity concerning Layer 2 and will also allow a comparison of ages of soft ocean sediments at different distances from the mid-ocean ridges. If continuous movement of the sea-floor is taking place, older sediments should be found at the edges of the oceans rather than in the middle. Early results seem to be bearing this out. Differences may be apparent between Layer 2 in what is probably primeval ocean in the Pacific, and the comparatively recent Atlantic Ocean. The drill may reach the volcanic material that forms the 'stripes' of the magnetic sea-floor pattern, and it may be possible to demonstrate the reversals of magnetization that are the probable cause of this symmetrical pattern. However, some magnetic measurements taken at the sea-bed, rather than from the sea-surface

Evidence for sea-floor spreading in the Pacific. Patterns of magnetic anomalies symmetrical about the axis of the ridge system are found to correlate with similarly symmetrical dating patterns. The keyed areas on the map represent rock ages in those regions where correlation has been demonstrated

20,000 feet above, show a very confused magnetic picture. A look at Iceland will suggest the reason why. There are hundreds of intrusive dykes separating the east and west portions of Iceland, and a similar state of affairs probably exists on the floor of the Atlantic. It is only when the results are smoothed by measuring the magnetic field a few miles above that the symmetrical 'wall-paper' pattern can be recognized. Random sampling by drilling may then merely provide an indeterminate result.

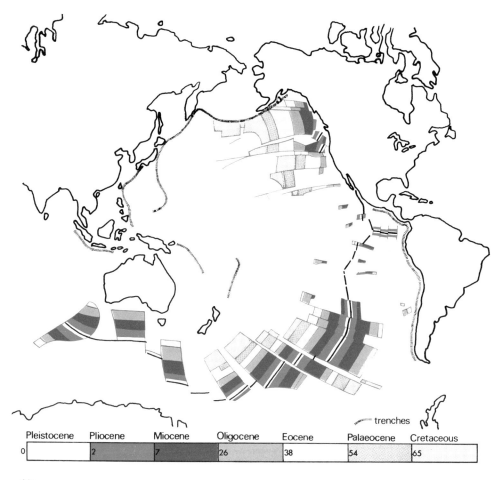

trenches

Pleistocene	Pliocene	Miocene	Oligocene	Eocene	Palaeocene	Cretaceous
0	2	7	26	38	54	65

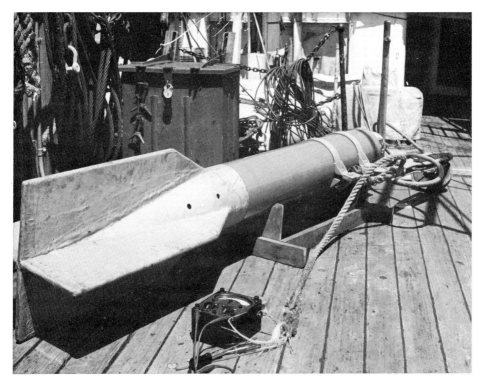

The JOIDES programme will sample continental slopes as well as the deep-ocean floor, and very possibly point the way to something of commercial value. It has been suggested that the large slumping and flow of sediments down continental slopes should have produced conditions favourable to the accumulation of oil. At present, this is highly speculative, but it is only by following curiously all the unknowns of the earth that we advance our ability to locate and extract the minerals that we need for modern life.

A magnetometer designed to detect magnetic anomalies in the sea-bed. When in use, it is towed astern of the research vessel

EARTHQUAKES AND VOLCANOES 6

Wooden croquet balls sometimes split as the wood dries out with age. The earth's surface also suffers splitting, but for other reasons. Whether one believes that the earth is still cooling down from its molten state, or whether, as is probable, it is in process of partial warming up, we do know that large quantities of heat are being generated in its interior and that, because the solid rock of the mantle and the crust is a bad conductor of heat, there will be differences in temperature producing large strains. These strains build up until something has to give, and the rock is torn in much the same way that a glass cracks when hot water is poured into it: the inside expands while the cool outer surface tries to maintain its shape. A readjustment of only a few inches involving many millions of tons of rock releases enormous energy. In a fraction of a second a burst of sound is produced which travels out as an earthquake wave.

An important cause of strains inside the earth is the drifting of the continental blocks on its surface. A solid block of continent tends to buckle when it pushes up against a less plastic obstacle; the front part takes the brunt of the shock like the mudguards of a car that runs into a brick wall.

The eruption of the Chilean volcano Phyehue, after the earthquake of June 1960

• seismic observatory
▲ volcano
▬ earthquake belt

Map locating the world's major earthquake belts, known active volcanoes, and seismic observatories

Sometimes, as we have seen, the continents are forced to split apart by slow-moving convection currents rising beneath them. Rift-valleys, which are conspicuous geographical features in Africa, are formed in this way. When the rock bends or is split apart, a sudden release of energy occurs at the critical moment of fracture, and the result is an earthquake. The effect can be simulated by bending a stick. At first, the stick bends without fuss, but suddenly it breaks with a sharp crack.

Several dozen large earthquakes are known to occur each year; they are detected by the network of seismographic observatories that covers the land surfaces. These observatories, which were established between fifty and eighty years ago, in order to learn more about the earth's structure, can detect minute earthquakes occurring nearby, and faint tremors from earthquake shocks that occur many thousands of miles away. A large earthquake will be registered by all observatories, while small shocks are only observable at a few local stations. Since the oceans cover two-thirds of the earth's surface, many small undersea shocks remain unobserved. However, something of the detailed activity beneath the sea-floor can be recorded on isolated islands.

Just as a stick only breaks in one place, so the earthquakes of the world are limited to specific zones. The earthquakes that take place in these zones relieve the strains set up in the earth, and so protect the rest of the world from damaging shock. For us today there are two main belts of activity. There is a narrow band circling the Pacific Ocean in which 80 per cent of the damaging earth shocks occur. The remainder tend to occur in a line running from Morocco through the north of the Mediterranean, Iran and the Himalayas, and down through south China to Indonesia, where it joins the circum-Pacific belt.

Japan lies in the zone of greatest earthquake activity, and an average of six major shocks are experienced there every year, with two or three minor shocks a day measurable on the sensitive seismograph. The large earthquakes in Japan are due to readjustments of rock masses which may take place near the surface or at depths as great as 400 miles. Half of these originate within 30 miles of the surface – that is, in the crustal rock layer and in the uppermost part of the mantle. The sites of origin of the other half are distributed fairly evenly below this depth, except for a notable lack of such points between the 50- and 100-mile depths. This is almost certainly due to the softening of the rock in the low-velocity layer delineated by the behaviour of the earthquake waves themselves.

Earthquakes occurring in the deep oceans follow well-defined lines. There is a belt of activity which follows the Mid-Atlantic Ridge from east of Greenland down to the latitude of the Falkland Islands. A continuation of this line runs into the Indian Ocean, where it turns northwards and finally swings right around to enter the Gulf of Aden. This loop is completed by a turn to the south down the rift-valley area of Africa. A subsidiary earthquake belt runs south-eastward from the middle of the Indian Ocean to meet the circum-Pacific belt at a point south of New Zealand. These ocean-earthquake zones give rise to smaller shocks than those that occur around the periphery of the Pacific or along the Alpine-Himalayan line, but they are of great interest in studying the mechanisms of earth movements because they follow the ridges of the ocean-floor. Modern ideas suggest that the sea-floors are moving away from central lines along which the upwelling convection currents occur. If the moving-sea-floor theory is correct, then it is at these central lines that earthquake activity would be expected. It is here that splits appear in the earth's crust, to be filled by volcanic lava pushed up from below.

The widening of the Atlantic Ocean is pushing the Americas westward, forcing their west coasts against various obstacles. The resulting buckling of the continental blocks produces breaks which manifest themselves as earthquakes. The whole of the west side of South America is a prolific earthquake area joining up with the active earthquake

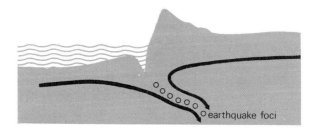

A simplified profile of the trench and earthquake belt off the west coast of the Americas, caused by a dipping down and sliding of the ocean-floor underneath the continental land masses

earthquake foci

area that runs through California to Alaska. On the western side of the Pacific the coastal fringes through Japan, the Philippines, the Solomons, Tonga, the Kermadec Trench and New Zealand include a high proportion of large earthquakes. This must be due in the first instance to convection-current activity tending to move the Asian block into the Pacific. We know that an eastward movement took place about 300-million years ago to separate India from Africa; we know also, from our fossil magnetism measurements, that Australia has been a wandering continent for hundreds of millions of years. The exact details of western Pacific movements have not yet been worked out, but the frequency and scale of earthquakes show that this is a part of the earth that is under great stress today.

Earthquake-prediction problems

The shock of rock breaking in an earthquake sends out a long train of waves of differing types lasting for many minutes. The first wave to arrive is the fast-travelling compressional or P wave, and, as we have seen, it is the observations

A British seismologist examines a seismogram recording shock waves received from a large earthquake

A seismograph at a Japanese observatory records similar waves

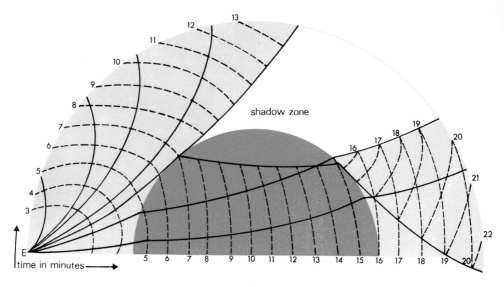

shadow zone

time in minutes →

A section through the earth showing the paths of seismic P waves emanating from an earthquake immediately below epicentre E, and the times in minutes elapsed before the waves reach various points on the earth's surface. No P waves reach the surface in the shadow zone, apparently because of refraction at the core-mantle junction

of this wave at various points on the earth that provide most information about the earth's crust, mantle and core. The small P wave is followed by other compressional waves that have suffered reflections at the interface between the mantle and the core. The next group of waves are the transverse or S waves, which can only travel in a solid, and which therefore suggest that the core is liquid. The main ground movements that can be felt during an earthquake are a group of 'surface' waves which cause the recording pen of the seismograph to swing slowly backwards and forwards with a period of many seconds. It is these waves which cause the destruction that is associated with earthquakes.

Although the breaking of rock that causes the earthquake shock-waves relieves strain that has been building up for years—perhaps hundreds of years—a tidying up process usually follows, in which minor readjustments of rock take place over a period of a few days. These cause a series of aftershocks which in some instances are large enough to add further destruction and confusion to that produced by the main shock. Sometimes small shocks precede large earthquakes, and at one time it was hoped that a careful recording of such precursors of the main event would provide early warning of danger. But although the problem of earthquake forecasting is being extensively investigated, no reliable system yet exists.

If rock under great strain inside the earth is on the point of breaking, it might be thought that any little extra force might tip the balance and trigger off an earthquake. For example, one earthquake shock might be expected to shake up rock layers in other places which were nearly at breaking point. There is some evidence that this does happen, but since we do not know when or where the triggering action will take place, it does not help in warning of disaster.

The gravitational attraction of the sun and moon also causes slight movements in the earth, and these 'earth tides' are in turn affected by the movement of water over the continental shelves as the ocean tides ebb and flow. They are also affected by changes in atmospheric pressure. But none of these external factors has definitely been associated with the triggering of earthquakes.

Rock under mounting strain may suddenly fracture, or 'fault', with an accompanying slight readjustment of position. A minor readjustment involving millions of tons of rock produces an earthquake. Below: sedimentary rock in Cornwall showing clear signs of faulting on a small scale

The strain in the earth can now be measured with delicate gauges, and the invention of the laser has led to a tool that can detect stress deformations over distances of many miles. Compression of rock causes an increase in the velocity of seismic waves, and there is some evidence that this shows up in measurements of earthquake waves. The build-up of pressure in a rock also changes the magnetic field in the rock, and there is evidence from Japan that magnetic-field observations can reveal such changes. However, accurate measurements close to the centre of an incipient earthquake would be needed for any form of warning to be possible.

The early-warning problem will become more acute as world population increases and people move into new areas in the active earthquake belts of the world. The recent oil discoveries in Alaska, for example, will undoubtedly attract a build-up of population in a place where some of the largest earth movements in recent years have taken place.

A 100-foot quartz rod, the sensor, or strain meter, of a strain seismograph designed to measure strains in the rock of Oahu, Hawaii

A rigid, steel and aluminium earth-quake-proof skyscraper in the course of construction in Tokyo, Japan

For those people, such as the Japanese, who are immediately above one of the more active zones, the building of shock-resisting houses is the only adequate precaution, and a great deal of Japanese effort has been devoted to the development of shockproof buildings. However, earthquake waves affecting cities are also liable to break gas and water mains, so creating a serious and virtually uncontrollable fire hazard. And epidemic disease may follow the disruption and pollution of a city's water supply. As a result mainly of the after-effects of the Tokyo earthquake of 1923, nearly 100,000 lives were lost.

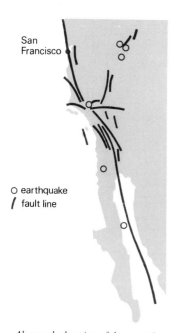

San Francisco

O earthquake

/ fault line

Above: the location of the great San Andreas Fault on the west coast of the United States. Opposite: an Apollo-9 infra-red photograph of a short stretch of the San Andreas Fault as, roughly parallel to the Colorado River, it enters the Gulf of California

A laconic reminder of the effects of severe earthquakes on cities: a San Francisco street sign in 1906

San Francisco is built on a famous scar on the earth's surface. This, the San Andreas Fault, can be traced deep into the crust, and the local rock has been torn and displaced for hundreds of miles during the past few million years. The fault is still active, and no doubt the strain is again building up, and will be relieved by a movement of a few feet during the next hundred years—perhaps much sooner. The last shock was in 1906, when a large part of the city was destroyed. Again, most of the damage was caused by fire which broke out after the earthquake shock.

The most catastrophic earthquake on record in terms of human lives lost occurred in China in 1556. Some 830,000 are said to have died. After four centuries the figure is naturally uncertain, but not impossible, because the earthquake was sited on the world's 'destruction belt', which runs from the Mediterranean area, through Iran and Central Asia to Japan. This belt owes its notoriety to the fact that it traverses many densely populated areas. Although most of the major earthquakes take place in the circum-Pacific belt, the majority of these affect only sparsely inhabited areas, or the sea.

Not only does the earth shake during an earthquake; sometimes the ground splits open as well. It was reported in the Quetta earthquake of 1935, which completely destroyed the town, that great chasms opened up in the ground, swallowing people and animals, and subsequently partially closing.

The Chile earthquake of 1960 was an example of a particularly severe and large tear in the earth's

surface. But because it occurred mostly in a wild mountainous part of the world, it did not kill more than 500 people. The active area covered a distance of about a thousand miles, and photographs show that the earth movements at the surface included both horizontal and vertical displacements. This shock was of great interest to seismologists because, perhaps on account of its vast extent, it set the earth as a whole vibrating like a struck bell. The Chilean earthquake activity extended to the sea-bed, and the movement there caused a 'tidal wave' which drowned another thousand people. Much flooding also took place due to changes in ground levels, and a volcano erupted two days after the main shock.

Volcanoes and lavas

Volcanoes have been the cause of as many of nature's terrifying catastrophies as have earthquakes. It is unfortunate that volcanoes often exist in places which have a pleasant climate; for this, together with the fertile soil that develops from volcanic debris, attracts human settlement close to the potential danger. Although it is often popularly believed that the lava that issues from a volcano comes from the liquid core of the earth, this is of course impossible. The core lies some 2,000 miles below the surface, and clearly it would be very difficult to think of a process whereby a thin pipe of molten material could move this great distance through the mantle, whose temperature is mainly below that of the melting point of rock.

We know from listening to the underground rumblings which volcanoes emit while the lava is forcing its way to the surface by fissuring the overlying rock, that the source of the molten rock is about thirty miles below the surface. In the

A granite 'dyke' formed by the intrusion of molten volcanic rock into fissures in an overlying slate bed

island of Hawaii a series of seismographs have detected micro-earthquakes associated with the eruptions of Mauna Loa and Kilauea for many years, and before one of the big outbursts the upward movement can be tracked by calculating the depths of these small shocks associated with the passage of lava.

There is another reason why we can be sure that volcanoes are not tapping a vast reservoir of liquid such as the core. A volcano only emits a limited amount of material at any one time, after which it lies quiescent. This indicates that there is a subterranean reservoir of molten rock which is limited in volume. Once some liquid has been drawn off, time must elapse before a new batch is heated up. The volcano source is rather like a boiler, with the vent to the surface acting as a safety valve to relieve the pressure that builds up when the boiler is heated. The source of heat is primarily that same radioactive heat which is continuously being generated in the crust and mantle, and which causes the softening that is supposed to characterize the low-velocity layer. It could be that it is the intermittent removal of large quantities of heat by volcanic action from the vicinity of the low-velocity layer that stops this layer from becoming a continuous belt of liquid.

There may be a secondary supply of heat, which in certain localities causes the upper parts of the nearly melting low-velocity layer to rise above the melting point. It is significant that the volcanoes of the world follow the zones of earthquake activity. These killing forces of nature are closely associated, and the reason probably is that the one causes the other. When rock movements occur inside the earth, the sudden break sends out energy in the form of earthquake waves. A great deal more energy almost certainly remains in the

Overleaf: a cooling lava flow, still partially molten, at Kilauea, Hawaii ▶

151

A monstrous 50-foot-high tongue of lava from the volcano Mauna Loa about to engulf the village of Hoopuloa, Hawaii, in 1926

neighbourhood of the rock fracture, because heat is generated when the rock surfaces move against each other. It has been known for a long time in seismic prospecting, where artificial earthquake waves are generated by explosions, that only a small fraction of the chemical energy of the explosion can be accounted for by adding up the contributions of all the seismic waves. If a similar mechanism takes place in earthquake-wave production, then a supply of heat, many times the energy that appears at the surface, remains underground. It is this heat which fuels the local underground melting pot at the base of the volcano.

Although the lava erupted from volcanoes comes from the mantle it does not provide us with more than a clue in our search for the composition of the mantle rock. This is because, in the process of melting, the constituents of the rock first fuse together, then gradually separate out into light and heavy material. This is known to happen because the lava that comes out of a volcano when young is different in composition from that extruded in its old age. In an island like Hawaii, which has been built entirely by volcanic action, the evidence can be seen lying at the surface. There are active volcanoes, and old extinct cones; and a careful examination of the lava-flows shows the gradual changes in erupted material that take place during a volcano's life. Examination of the lava shows that another factor has been at work to confuse the evidence concerning the composition of mantle rock. While the molten rock from the mantle is forcing its way to the surface, following cracks in the rock, and widening them by its pressure, it melts some of the rock through which it travels, and incorporates crustal rock material into its own molten stream.

Part of the pahoehoe lava flow on the Kau desert south of Kilauea, Hawaii. Pahoehoe lava, which produces this syrup-like formation, contrasts with the slag-like character of a-a lava

A 'lavafall' on the volcanic island Surtsey as the latter rears up out of the Atlantic near Iceland

There may be places in the world where such vast quantities of molten rock have come up from the mantle that the mixing with crustal rocks was negligible and the separation into light and heavy fractions did not have time to take place. Some geologists believe that St Paul's Rocks in the Atlantic are the result of such an outpouring, but there is always a doubt about what did take place, and there is still a possibility that the process of melting and resolidification changed the constitution of the original mantle material. Other similar large volumes of rock which have flowed up to the surface from the mantle are to be found as giant batholiths in many large mountain ranges. The once molten material has certainly come from inside the earth, and it has played an important part in building the mountain structure, but whether it represents mantle in its original form will not be known until we bore into the mantle itself and collect a virgin sample for comparison with what can be seen at the surface.

Volcanic islands

Volcanoes can be great destroyers of life. Vesuvius sprang an unpleasant surprise in AD 79, when it completely covered Pompeii with hot ash and pumice in less than two days. Many people were trapped, overcome by the heat and fumes. Although the volcano had been quiet from the earliest recorded times, warning earthquake shocks had taken place in the vicinity of the Bay of Naples in the preceding sixteen years. After the destruction of Pompeii, Vesuvius continued to be intermittently eruptive for a thousand years. A period of peacefulness occurred between 1139 and 1631, but, to demonstrate that volcanoes are not to be trusted, the activity started up once more, and eruptions have occurred ever since. The last was in 1944, and if past experience is any guide, a new outburst is overdue.

In 1902 the small volcanic mountain called Pelée in the pleasant Caribbean island of Martinique, literally burst apart. The city of Saint-Pierre, called 'the Paris of the West Indies' was smothered by a cloud of superheated gases and glowing particles which burst from the mountainside and killed the 30,000 inhabitants within three or four minutes.

A night view of the lava lake formed in the crater of the Niragongo volcano in the Belgian Congo

Plaster casts of a dog and a man — victims of the eruption of Vesuvius in 79 AD — recovered during modern excavations at Pompeii

A well-documented modern eruption took place some years ago in the Azores, those fertile volcanic islands that lie on the earthquake belt of the Mid-Atlantic Ridge. Showers of ash were gradually engulfing the local lighthouse when the government, with a stroke of genius, changed the job of lighthouse keeper to that of volcano observer. The ex-lighthouse keeper was provided with a camera, and obtained an excellent and beautiful pictorial record of the birth of a new piece of land.

Similar photographic cover has been obtained at the other end of the Mid-Atlantic Ridge, where the island of Surtsey has grown out of the sea near Iceland.

These present-day demonstrations of the building forces of nature are of great interest to geologists in showing how rapidly some changes in the earth's surface take place. Although processes of erosion and deposition to form new rock strata are slow and extend over millions of years, the catastrophic happening also plays an important part in geological history.

Islands like Surtsey in the Atlantic are subjected to attack by the sea as soon as they raise their heads above the surface. However, after many years of alternating building and washing away, the volcano generally wins because although some of the erupted material is in the form of ash, which is easily washed away by the waves, there is also a solid core of lava which soldifies to form a tough basalt rock difficult to erode. There is an additional hazard to islands in the Pacific Ocean. The volcano grows from the sea-bed, finally emerging above the surface of the sea. Mauna Loa in Hawaii, for example, now rises 13,600 feet above sea-level, so that measured from the sea-bed it is taller than Mount Everest. It would be taller still, but for the fact that all the deep-ocean Pacific volcanoes, of which there are hundreds, gradually subside several thousand feet into the sea-floor. It is possible that they fall back into the void left by the lava that has been erupted, but it is more likely that they overstrain the thin oceanic crust, and therefore sink until their weight is balanced by plastic mantle material displaced in the softer part of the upper mantle.

The evidence for the sinking of volcanic islands in the Pacific is based on the formation of coral atolls and flat-topped sea-mounts, or guyots. The latter are volcanic peaks rising from the sea-floor. Instead of having the familiar conical shape that is associated with volcanoes, guyots have had their

Surtsey only a few days after its sudden and spectacular birth over the northernmost region of the Mid-Atlantic Ridge

The Wase Rock in Nigeria, a large volcanic plug exposed by the erosion of surrounding rock less resistant to weathering

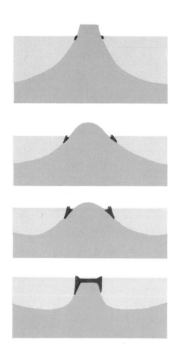

Above: the stages in the formation of the coral atoll. Opposite: Capricorn Group Island, part of the Great Barrier Reef, viewed from the air (top), and from the coral reef encircling it (bottom)

tops cut off. They suffered this truncation due to wave action when they were still young and active enough to rise above sea-level. The subsequent sinking under their own weight has produced the flat tops submerged several hundred fathoms below the sea surface.

The same sinking process accounts for coral atolls. In the tropics coral reefs grow round volcanic islands to form a fringing reef. If the island sinks, the coral will continue to grow upward to stay near sea-level where it can survive. Corals can only live and grow in warm, salt water less than 200 feet deep. They grow well on the outer side of the reef, but not so rapidly on the side adjacent to the island, since mud brought down by rain tends to choke them. As the island sinks, therefore, a lagoon is formed, at first containing a central island. This phase of development of atolls can be seen in Pacific islands such as Bora-Bora. However, volcanic islands usually sink several thousand feet before they float in a state of equilibrium in the plastic mantle layer, and often they disappear, leaving only the coral ring of the familiar atoll. This explanation of coral-atoll formation has been confirmed by seismic prospecting experiments in the lagoons of atolls, and by drilling.

It is an interesting contrast to find that the coral rock around the volcanic island of Bermuda in the Atlantic is only a few hundred feet thick. This means that Bermuda has not subsided like islands in the Pacific. The thickness of coral at Bermuda can be readily explained by changes of sea-level during ice-ages. Why Pacific volcanoes find their own level, as if floating in the plastic mantle, while Atlantic volcanoes stay in their growing position, is not clear. It does point to a difference between Atlantic and Pacific, just as we might

expect if the Atlantic has been formed by continental drift quite recently in the earth's history, while the Pacific is part of the original ocean basin formed over 4,000-million years ago when Mars and the moon parted company with the earth. Perhaps the separation of the continents has left some continental material on the Atlantic floor. Seismic measurements do show that Layer 2 is thicker under the Atlantic than the Pacific, and this could provide sufficient rigidity to resist the sinking of Atlantic islands. If continents can plough their way through the oceanic crust, as must be the case if continental drift is possible, continental rock must be less yielding than sub-oceanic crust.

Another island group that has only a few hundred feet thickness of coral is the Seychelles, in the Indian Ocean, but the explanation here, as we have seen, is that these islands are a fragment of granitic continental rock which once formed part of Africa and India.

A natural mud pool lazily churning and bubbling near Rotorua, New Zealand

Catastrophic eruptions

Volcanoes are benevolent for the greater part of their lives, and the warmth and good soil which they provide probably outweigh the intermittent damage they cause. Hot springs associated with volcanically active areas have provided baths of reputed medicinal value in Greece and Italy from the earliest historical times. Resorts like Dogo in Japan and Rotorua in New Zealand are centred on such facilities. Iceland is also famous for its geysers which spout streams of steam and water into the air at regular intervals. For many years at Ladorello in Italy underground steam wells have tapped the hot rock a few thousand feet below the surface to bring high-pressure steam to turbines driving electricity generators. There are many other places in the world where a combination of hot fissured rock and a supply of underground water produce a reservoir of steam. The energy-producing capacities of such underground stores of steam are of the same order of magnitude as oilfields, and since production is by bore-holes some of the oilfield technology is being applied to the search for steam. Commercial production has been satisfactory in New Zealand for ten years or more; Hawaii also has sources of natural steam power; and many other volcanic areas of the world are awaiting development.

Earthquakes, because of the heat generated when underground rock layers are ground together, help to produce volcanoes. Conversely, some volcanic eruptions are so explosive that they produce earthquake waves. In 1883 one of the largest explosions the world has ever heard took place in the Sunda Straits, between Java and Sumatra. The island of Krakatoa literally disintegrated, leaving a crater some three and a half miles across and about a thousand feet deep. Before the event, the island projected at least a thousand feet above sea-level, so that several cubic miles of rock were ejected during the explosion. The bulk of this material fell over hundreds of square miles in the vicinity of the volcano, and the sky was darkened for several days by the falling ash. But for some years throughout the world sunset skies were brilliantly coloured as a result of dust clouds persisting at a height between 100,000 and 120,000 feet.

The explosive type of volcano, as opposed to the more gentle type of eruption that occurs in the Pacific islands, pours out almost all of its solid matter in the form of dust, hot gases and boulders. This is because the molten lava from the upper

'Old Faithful', the famous geyser at Yellowstone National Park in Wyoming, once again blows on time

163

Three kinds of volcanic eruption, in ascending order of violence. 1: a 'quiet' eruption, in which magma welling up in the central core simply flows through a side vent. 2: an explosive eruption, in which hot cinders and gases are ejected through the core under great pressure. 3: a catastrophic eruption involving the virtual disintegration of the entire cone

part of the mantle has assimilated a large proportion of the lighter crustal rock material, and with it steam- and gas-forming materials. In volcanoes that occur in thin-crust oceanic areas, more than two-thirds of the energy released is brought to the surface in the form of molten rock. The situation may have been aggravated in the case of Krakatoa by sea-water pouring into the initially formed crater, and cooling the lava to produce a strong cap, which withstood the internal pressure until the strength of the rock was exceeded and the top blew off.

Krakatoa had erupted violently hundreds of years earlier, the last recorded activity before the cataclysm of 1883 occurring in 1680. However, volcanoes generally give signs of their reawakening, and those who can interpret the nature of local earthquake activity today might well have been able to warn of the disaster, which led to the deaths of more than 100,000 people. The explosive eruption on August 27 had been preceded that May by some volcanic activity, just as the killing phase of the Mount Pelée eruption had been preceded by milder emissions of steam and gas. It is possible that these violent eruptions are the result of the cooling of a large underground chamber of molten rock. Heat is evolved in the process of solidification of the liquid, and this builds up a great pressure in volatile crustal materials. This process may take a long time, but the moral is to be wary of dormant volcanoes, especially when they begin to grumble and show signs of leaks at the surface.

A rival to Krakatoa in scale of activity was Mount Katmai in the Aleutian Islands. In 1912 an area of 53 square-miles was covered to a depth of 700 feet by hot particles thrown out when a new volcano, Novarupta, six miles away, drained

Katmai's liquid rock reservoir, Mount Katmai collapsed, and the 'Valley of 10,000 Smokes' appeared where the hot ash deposit generated steam as it came in contact with ground water. There may have been even larger explosions in the past. It is estimated that in the volcanic area of New Zealand, 5,000 square-miles was once thickly covered by volcanic material, and that 200 cubic miles of solids were belched into the air.

Tsunamis, or 'tidal waves'

Krakatoa behaved in very much the same way as a large man-made explosion, and the seismic waves it caused were recorded in many parts of the world. An estimate of the equivalent size of high explosive can be made from the diameter of the crater, and this ranks Krakatoa with a 50-megaton nuclear device. The explosion produced

The destructive potential of a tsunami as it enters coastal waters, vividly expressed by the early nineteenth-century Japanese artist Hokusai in his woodcut The Great Wave off Kanagawa. *(In the background is the volcano Fujiyama)*

a great wave – the common expression is 'tidal wave', but since these phenomena have nothing to do with tides, the better term is 'tsunami', of Japanese origin. The size of such waves produced by underwater explosions, has also been related to the weight of explosive charge, and a calculation for Krakatoa based on this reasoning confirms the figure obtained for the crater size. The wave was 135 feet high when it smothered the village of Merak, 53 miles from Krakatoa. Forty miles west of Krakatoa, the water had surged to 50 feet above sea-level as it swept past a lighthouse, but since the light was situated on an arm of land, this was probably the height of the deep-water wave, which would normally steepen and increase in height on reaching shallow water.

Tsunamis are often the cause of more deaths than the volcanoes or earthquakes themselves. The famous Lisbon earthquake of 1755, in which

A contemporary record of a tsunami that struck the coast of northwestern Europe in 1613 with disastrous effect

40,000 people were killed, took place at the coast, and the ground movement again caused a great surge of water, which accounted for more than half the casualties. These tsunamis travel at speeds of several hundred miles an hour across the deep oceans, and may be almost imperceptible to a ship at sea, since the rise and fall of the sea surface is generally only a few feet in the course of 20 minutes. Tsunamis become vicious when they reach shallow water: the front of the wave is slowed up so that the rest of the water piles up to form a wall fifty feet or more in height, which roars across the land felling everything in its path. Tsunamis have caused great havoc in Japan and Hawaii in the past, but now a warning system is in operation. Seismograph observers who report earthquakes are aware of the potential danger of any earthquake at sea or on the coast, and when such earthquakes are recorded the possibility of a tsunami is noted. The tsunami travels at hundreds of miles an hour, but earthquake-wave velocities are measured in miles per second, so that earthquakes are recorded virtually instantaneously, while a tsunami will take hours to cross an ocean. There is ample time to arrange evacuation from low-lying coastal areas which may be affected, and the inconvenience is short lived, since the calculations are precise.

However, warnings are not always heeded. Curiosity overcame proper caution some years ago in California, when, instead of rushing to high ground following a tsunami warning, local inhabitants poured down to the beach to see this rare phenomenon. Fortunately the wave was much smaller than expected.

How volcanoes can build massive features such as the Pacific Islands is apparent because we can see volcanic processes in operation today. What of the even larger features of the earth's surface–the great mountain ranges such as the Himalaya, the Alps, the Andes and the Rockies, that rise to heights of several miles above sea-level? The answer to the question of how mountains were formed is not difficult to grasp if we think of the earth as a whole, rather than looking upwards at the grandeur of the mountain and valley complex from our Lilliputian plainsman's viewpoint. The five-mile-high Mount Everest fades into insignificance when considered in relation to the 8,000-mile diameter earth. On a six-foot-diameter model of the earth, the crust would only be as thick as a layer of adhesive plaster. The school-room globes that show mountain ranges in elevation have their vertical scale greatly exaggerated. Continental cross-sections drawn in text-books of necessity make the sloping surfaces appear much too steep. Deep ocean trenches are often drawn as almost vertically sided chasms; yet the deepest of them all, the Challenger Deep (35,800 feet) in the Marianas Trench, looks quite gentle when portrayed in its proper proportions.

Opposite: satellite views of two of the earth's greatest mountain ranges. Top: a detail of the Himalayas–a range which apparently owes its existence to the ramming by India of the main Asian land mass. Bottom: the Andes in the region of Lake Titicaca in Bolivia

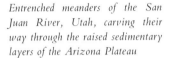

Entrenched meanders of the San Juan River, Utah, carving their way through the raised sedimentary layers of the Arizona Plateau

Mountains and valleys on the surface of the earth are little more than wrinkles in the skin of an old apple. As with the apple, they may have been formed by a shrinking of the interior, leaving too large a skin, which adjusts to the change by forming a series of folds. This was the early theory of mountain building, and it was based on the idea of a contracting earth, which decreased in volume because it cooled. The shortening of the earth's crust was measured by adding up the distance saved due to all the folded rocks that make up the mountains and valleys. A length of a few hundred miles was obtained, but this is much too great to be accounted for by a change in size of the earth resulting from a cooling down of the mantle. A plausible explanation of the observed shrinkage of the crust can be found if it is assumed that the liquid core has developed from mantle material by a changing of the solid mantle into a liquid with a volume smaller than that of the parent rock. Such a change of state in the earth-building material may have occurred, but our knowledge is not yet sufficient to be sure what was the true course of events. It is extremely

difficult to compress rock in the laboratory to determine what changes take place under extreme conditions of temperature and pressure. However, attempts at this type of experiment are being made.

A change in rock from one state to another by heat and pressure has been suggested as the panacea for all problems associated with the earth's structure. The lower basaltic part of the crust could be a lighter form of mantle rock, and one could imagine the crust thickening in some places as it was formed from mantle material. This would explain large raised areas of the continents such as are found in Tibet and Arizona. The extra thickness of lighter crustal rock would rise up because it is floating like a giant iceberg in the plastic mantle.

No one is certain whether the earth has been cooling down and contracting, or heating up and expanding. If a large increase in the size of the earth has taken place, a ready explanation is available for the distribution of land over only one-third of its surface. An original crust which once uniformly covered the earth could split at the 'seams' as the size of the earth increased, leaving the continents as they are today. Mountains and rifts could have been caused by local horizontal forces pushing and pulling on the thin fragments of crustal skin during the earth's growth. This simple idea gives an easy explanation for the fit of the continents – one of the main lines of evidence in favour of continental drift – and also for the difference between oceanic and continental crusts. A continued expansion could, moreover, be the reason for the spreading of the ocean-floors from the mid-ocean ridges. The ultimate cause of the expansion of the earth could be the heat produced by radioactivity but, even if this is so, there still appears to be a large numerical discrepancy: an increase in radius of about two inches a century would be needed to change a small earth, with continents covering the whole surface, to the present larger sphere with land masses occupying only three-tenths, whereas the most reliable estimates of expansion due to heating restrict the rate of increase in radius to no more than a fraction of an inch in a hundred years.

The great mountain ranges

Probably the most reasonable way to account for the topographical features of the earth is to follow the story that has been outlined in earlier chapters. A cloud of dust and gases condenses to form a cold earth which melts at an early stage, throwing off Mars and the moon after a crustal layer and a liquid core have separated, and is left with a single continental mass. The subsequent break-up of this single continent and the drifting apart of the separate new land masses under the action of some form of slow movement in the plastic mantle can now account for all mountain ranges, valleys and rifts. There is no great difficulty in

Opposite: the location of the world's great mountain ranges. The shaded areas represent land over 3,000 feet above sea-level.

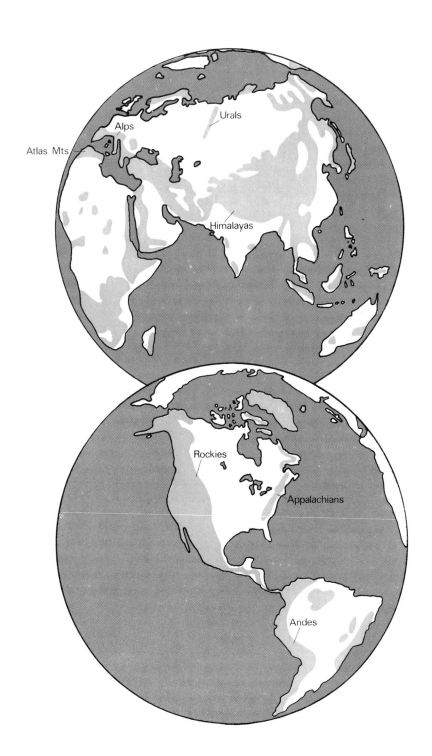

explaining the confused arrangement of these surface features, since movements of continents will have occurred over thousands of millions of years, and in many different directions.

There are in fact many regularities in the more conspicuous chains of mountains. The Rockies of North America and the Andes of South America both form lengthy chains along the western sides of their respective continents. This is exactly what we should expect if the Americas have been driven westward into the originally much more extensive Pacific Ocean. The continents crumple at their leading edges where they are being forced into the Pacific Ocean crust, rather than on their Atlantic coasts where the gentle push is being applied. The Pacific crust itself is probably moving to the east due to its own driving forces, and the big mountain ranges are the result of these two opposing pressures. It is probable that the American continents have ridden over considerable areas of the original Pacific floor, and the heating up of this oceanic crust as it was thrust down into the hotter mantle rock could have given rise to volcanic activity.

On the Atlantic side of this American drift we have the massive underwater mountain range of the Mid-Atlantic Ridge which, as we have seen, appears to be fed by an upwelling source of molten material, which manifests itself above water in Iceland. Africa, on the other hand, does not appear to have encountered a continental obstacle, or a sea-floor resisting its movement. By drifting too far to the east, however, it has overrun another upward movement in the plastic mantle. It is being split along a roughly north-south line running from the Red Sea down through the conspicuous east-African rift-valleys. Before this eastward drift, which took place about

150-million years ago Africa lay to the west of
this particular upwelling of the mantle, and suffered an earlier splitting when southern India, the
Seychelles micro-continent and Madagascar drifted away from southern Africa. Because of the
nature of the continental and sea-floor movements, the African coastline facing the Atlantic
Ocean is peaceful. The continent is riding with
the sea-floor, and there is no conflict with the
oceanic crust.

That the mountains of north Africa and southern Europe run in a general east-west direction, is
the result of a northerly push by Africa against
Europe. The Alps, formed only 20-million years
ago, form one of the youngest of the world's large
mountain systems and reflect the later part of the
northward movement of Europe demonstrated

A panoramic view of the Alps in central Switzerland

by the results of fossil magnetism in places like the North Sea. To the north of India, where the southern Indian fragment, broken off from Africa, has been forcing its way northwards, the Himalayan complex was produced.

Some mountain ranges, such as the Pyrenees or the Moroccan series, end when they reach the coast, because the folding of the thin continental skin meets the different crustal region of the ocean. Some old mountain ranges on one side of the Atlantic can be linked with counterparts on the opposite side, since they were one before drift separated their respective continents.

Mountain-building periods

Traces of old mountain ranges can be seen in many parts of the earth, but the exact details of the continental movements which produced them have yet to be worked out. The evidence becomes obscured when it has suffered hundreds of millions of years of erosion, and when tilting and warping of the thin continental plates has formed shallow seas which have collected new sedimentary rock layers. It is fairly certain, however, that mountain building has occurred during several fairly distinct periods of activity separated by times of quiescence. The activity has not necessarily occurred at the same time all over the world; on the contrary, the evidence points to one region taking its turn and undergoing a topographical face-lift, and then lying dormant while another part of the earth's surface suffers disruption, mountain building and a large outpouring of molten rock from the mantle.

These periods of activity have occurred in recent geological times, and may even be more frequent now than they were in the distant past. This fact is difficult to explain if we assume that mountain

Opposite: a time chart showing the major mountain-building periods during the past 520-million years

building is caused by a cooling, shrinking earth, since the cooling would be expected to be more rapid in the earlier days than it is now and the time between fresh outbursts would become longer as the earth grew older. There is no objection on this score, however, if the mechanism is one of drifting continents driven by fluid movements in the near-molten mantle. The best assessments of the radioactive heat that is being produced inside the earth tally closely with the measurement of heat coming out through the surface. There is probably a slight excess of heat production, which is having the effect of warming the low-velocity layer in the upper part of the mantle. This layer of nearly melted rock will gradually move towards the surface as the heat is conducted upwards, and when at a critical depth, will be in a position to start a new outburst of mountain-building activity. Melting will take place as the pressure due to overlying rock becomes less, and the conditions for circulating currents and upwelling will be present. Continents will be forced apart, resistance to movement will cause buckling of the crust into mountains. Large quantities of molten rock will be forced to the surface to form the gigantic batholiths which are to be found in the core of mountain ranges, and the earth's excess internal heat will have been temporarily removed. The upper mantle will become truly solid once more, and a new phase of build-up of radioactive heat can commence.

The internal heat is not necessarily relieved at the same time at all parts of the earth, so that the observed regional activity as well as the separate periods of mountain building are just what would be expected. It is possible that the crumpling of the edges of the continents to form such mountain ranges as the Andes is partially due to the push

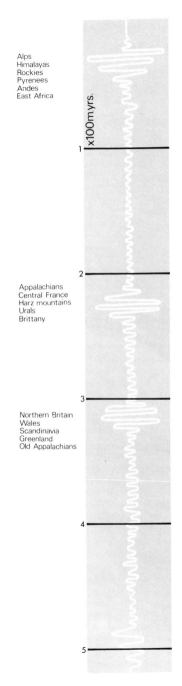

being continued, in this case from the Mid-Atlantic Ridge, while a temporary halt has been caused by a lag in the rise of the near molten layer beneath the appropriate parts of the Pacific ocean floor. We do not yet know enough about the details of these movements: we do not know whether slow convection currents are always at work in the mantle, or whether vast pockets of nearly molten material trigger off the active periods of mountain building. It is certain only that the internal radioactive heat provides the motive power, and that there is enough energy inside the earth to keep the process going. Many mountain ranges are formed of sediments which have been lifted up from beneath the shallow fringing continental seas, and it is possible that the formation of thick sediment deposits may automatically initiate a melting cycle. The badly conducting blanket of sediments would hold back the earth's outward flow of heat, and may contribute to the local melting. The depression which attracted the thick layers of sediment in the first place may have been caused by a sideways squeezing out of the more plastic layer of the upper mantle.

A temperature probe about to be lowered to the floor of the Pacific

Measurements of the heat escaping from the inside of the earth show that the average flow of heat is the same through the sea-floor as it is at the surface of the land. This fact requires an explanation, since the radioactivity of crustal rocks is greater than that of the mantle, and therefore more heat is being produced under the continents than under the oceans. For the same amount of heat to flow in these two different areas it is necessary to have a higher temperature nearer the surface under the sea-floor. This is probably the case, since the low-velocity layer, which, as we have seen, is a zone of near melting of the upper mantle, is closer to the surface under the sea than under continents. The proximity of the hot low-velocity layer to the sea-bed could give rise to the upward flow of liquid along the centre lines of the oceans, followed by the process of outward spreading of the ocean-floor. If the present-day situation regarding heat-flow is the normal one for the earth, the low-velocity layers beneath oceans and continents are presumably at different depths because the steady heat-flow is from the bulk of the mantle. There must be some mechanism for removal of the heat produced in the crustal rocks, more particularly the heat from continental blocks. One explanation could be intermittent excessive heat-flows associated with local upwelling from the low-velocity layer. This is manifested on continents by the vast batholith type outflows of molten rock, which are associated with mountain building, and more regularly on a smaller scale by the mid-ocean volcanic intrusions.

Some old mountains are almost flattened out today, yet a careful examination of the rocks shows that they have not been ground down to the roots. Perhaps some form of plastic collapse has taken place, and the peaks have spread out

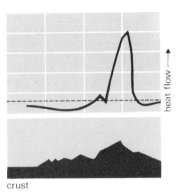

heat flow ⟶

crust

Diagram illustrating the relative increase in sea-bed temperature observed while tracking across the Mid-Atlantic Ridge

lava field

batholiths

Map showing the series of gigantic North American batholiths that intruded through the crust during the mid-Cretaceous period, about 100-million years ago

Opposite: the relative lengths of the half-lives of some isotopes useful for geological dating by radioactive means

sideways like a lump of pitch, flattened out by the pull of the earth's gravitational attraction. This type of gravitational collapse may have been responsible for some of the folding that shows up as foothills on the flanks of large mountain ranges. These foothills could be the result of a sideways force due to a tendency for the mountain rock to flow downhill. They could also be wrinkles formed to accommodate the large quantities of molten rock which push up into the centre of mountains, and bulge the newly formed mountain outwards.

Rock dating

The mountain and valley scenery of the world is the result primarily of the action of the earth's internal heat engine, but minor modifications are produced by climate, the sea and gravitational forces. The enormous variety of rock formations are matched by the vast number of combinations of circumstances which could possibly have produced them over the geological times of hundreds of millions of years. The chronological order in which sedimentary rocks were deposited can be determined by an examination of the fossil remains, the oldest of which are more than half as old as the earth itself. A clock that reaches back even further, to the first solidification of the earth, is provided by radioactivity, the very force that causes all the surface changes in the earth.

With the passing of time, radioactive uranium, thorium and potassium atoms decay. In doing so, not only do they provide energy which keeps the mantle and crust warm, but they also change into different elements. Uranium and thorium change into lead, while potassium atoms lose one electron each and become atoms of the rare gas argon. If we examine a rock which contains uranium, there will invariably be some associated lead which has been formed in the course of the hundreds of millions of years that have elapsed since the uranium was deposited. We know, from measurements in the laboratory, that in 700-million years half of the original uranium – if it is uranium of atomic number 235 – will have become a lead isotope of atomic number 207. Thus if we analyse the uranium mineral and find the relative quantities of lead and uranium we can determine the date at which the uranium was first concentrated from the molten rock. Unfortunately the dating is not quite as simple as this, for in the first place there are two types of radioactive uranium (the second type, uranium 238, decays more slowly, having a 'half-life' of 4,500-million years). Then there are several different lead atoms, so that age-dating calls for a separation of the rock constituents not merely into different chemical elements, but into atoms of different masses. Thus we must separate lead of 208 mass, which is derived from radioactive thorium, from leads 207 and 206, which are the end-products of uranium decay, and from lead 204, which appears to be a lead with no radioactive ancestry.

Although the lead picture is confused, the fact that there are several different radioactive decay mechanisms in operation makes it possible to make more than one age determination on a rock which contains lead. Agreement between results obtained by different methods tends to confirm the ages calculated. However, the rocks are thousands of millions of years old, so that there will have been many opportunities for the evidence to be spoilt by loss of some of the relevant materials. Furthermore, some original lead, not derived from radioactive decay of uranium or thorium, is generally present in lead minerals. This primordial

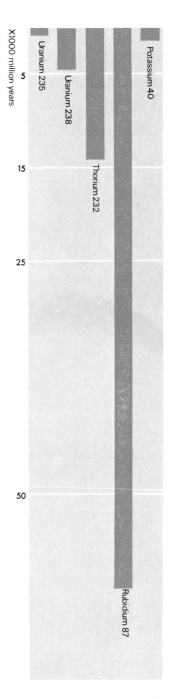

lead may be similar to that found in some meteorites; if this is so, the age of the oldest lead that has been investigated is about 4,500- to 5,000-million years old. This we may take as the age at which the earth's crust solidified.

Two other useful radioactive 'clocks' are available. It is known that half an original quantity of the element rubidium changes to strontium in 50,000-million years, a much slower rate than the uranium and thorium timing mechanisms. An intermediate rate of decay is provided by potassium which takes 13,000-million years for half its atoms to change to argon. Many measurements are now being made on rocks from all parts of the crust by means of these new dating methods. Most of the ages correspond to events such as the cooling of lava or the recrystallization of minerals which have taken place as the crust took on its present configuration: they can therefore be used to mark in time the big changes that have occurred, such as periods of active mountain building.

In some instances a piece of rock will appear to have been formed at a certain time, but its microscopic components will be found to have a different age. By working in this manner on the large and on the microscopic fragments of geological history, it is becoming possible to unravel what has been happening during the past 4,500-million years, especially as the radioactive dates of events can be compared with the sequences that the animal and plant fossils reveal.

The continental drift hypothesis affords a ready explanation of fossil distribution in old rocks. The work on radioactive-age determination and on the magnetic-field direction in old rocks makes it possible to chart a reasonable series of movements of the land masses of the earth. If we regard the continents as moving slowly about the earth's surface, we can see how buckling produces mountains when resistance is encountered; why wrinkling due to internal movements in the mantle will also form mountains, while tensions caused by rising currents cause rifts in the crust. We are still amassing data about the earth's radioactivity, its magnetism, gravitational field and its electrical conductivity, and the picture of what has been happening during the life of the earth is steadily clearing. Each new discovery in the earth sciences causes an exciting reappraisal of the evidence. For example, the discovery of the magnetic patterns on the rocks of the ocean-floor provided the clue to the moving-crust concept, but there are some anomalies that must still be explained. Among them is the fact that the magnetic pattern disappears as the borders of the Atlantic are reached. Is this because the sediments are thicker here, or because the magnetized volcanic rocks which have spread from the central ridge of the Atlantic have dived deep beneath the continental margins and become demagnetized because of high temperature? If the history of past discoveries is any guide, the investigation of these exceptions to the theory will provide further facts and throw new light on our understanding of the earth.

Although most of the deductions that have been made about the composition of the inside of the earth are based on natural phenomena that are measured at the surface, there is one tool that can be operated under controlled conditions to probe into the earth's mysteries. This is the 'seismic' method, an extension of observations of random earthquakes to particular experiments in which searching seismic waves are sent out from man-made explosions underground. The coming of the nuclear age has doubly furthered the exploration of the crust, mantle and core by means of subterranean shock waves. In the first place, the development of very powerful nuclear bombs has made it possible to stage controlled explosions detectable right around the world and, secondly, the effort spent in locating alien underground nuclear tests has enormously improved techniques of detecting seismic waves.

The new atomic sources of seismic waves are as effective as large earthquakes in sending waves around and through the earth, but they have the great advantage over earthquakes in that the position and instant of detonation are both exactly known. Unless an earthquake happens to originate close to several observing stations, there is an

Opposite: a nuclear test explosion in the Nevada Desert. Knowledge of the exact time and place of several such detonations has enabled seismologists to determine with great accuracy the behavior of the resulting shock waves

uncertainty of a few seconds in calculating when the shock started, and of a few miles in fixing its site of origin. Furthermore, planned experiments enable instruments to be placed where measurements will be most effective in elucidating controversial interpretations of the earth's internal structure. For example, in order to learn for certain whether a solid inner core exists, waves that

A seismogram collating the traces of vibrations received from the same underground explosion by an array of twenty-four seismometers

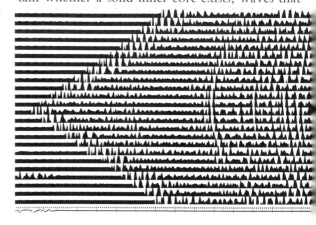

Below: the Sedan Crater, produced by an underground nuclear explosion in the Nevada Desert

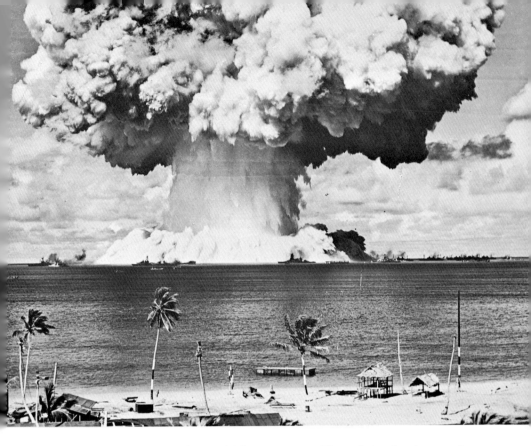

pass through the core and others which may reflect from an inner core are being studied. The
effect of the low-velocity layer, is evident at places
within about 2,000 miles of the explosion.

The Pacific nuclear tests of the 1940s were recorded at the far side of the world by earthquake
seismographs. Unfortunately, in those days, the
secrecy which enveloped all atomic-bomb opera-
tions prevented the military from announcing the
exact time of detonation of the weapon, although
the restricted press coverage did pinpoint the
location of the blast. This lack of information
would have meant a loss of some of the advantage
to be gained from controlled explosions, but for
the ingenuity of one scientist who reasoned, cor-
rectly as it turned out, that the military mind

*The explosion of a pioneer nuclear
device detonated at Bikini in the
Pacific in 1946*

could be expected to time so important a detonation exactly on the minute. The earthquake recordings themselves gave the instant of explosion to within a few seconds, and the exact-minute assumption did the rest.

More recent tests have been planned to allow for the positioning of portable recorders in addition to the world network of seismograph stations. Seismographs have also been designed which can record on the ocean-floor, a place where disturbance due to extraneous man-made noise is small. In the future, large underground explosions may be used to allow international investigations of particular geophysical problems, such as the structure of the inner core; and careful planning and cooperation of the type that has proved most successful in a smaller way in studying the roots of the Alps will ensure that the maximum benefit is obtained from each shot.

The world-wide pattern of seismological observations that has taught us so much, both about

A portable seismic observatory, consisting of a self-powered seismometer and seismograph, that can be set up almost anywhere and be left unattended for up to ten days

earthquakes themselves and about the internal structure of the earth, was established towards the end of the nineteenth century, largely through the efforts of the British Association for the Advancement of Science. There had been little change until the present nuclear age; but now, with the backing of vast defence budgets, a new era of seismological science has dawned and fundamental research will reap the reward provided by better instrumentation and more elaborate experiments. This reward will be well deserved; for although the study of earthquake-wave travel provides mental stimulation rather than practical comforts, seismic waves have been for many years adapted to finding oil. The seismic-reflection method is the primary tool of the oil geologist for locating underground structures of a shape and size likely to form reservoirs of oil. Over the past thirty years the instruments and theory of the seismic method have been refined, enabling deeper and more accurate probing into the ground. These improvements, and the increased understanding gained in research into the seismic method by the oil companies proved of inestimable value in the 1950s when a crash programme was directed to the detection of underground nuclear explosions in an effort to formulate a workable nuclear test-ban treaty.

The first problem in bomb detection is to record the signal from the bomb in the face of unwanted 'noise' produced by men and vehicles, wind shaking the trees, waves pounding on the beach and the many other background effects that can be detected with sensitive instruments in what appear to be quiet places. A ground movement of less than a millionth of an inch is readily observable with modern apparatus, and in order to enhance the signal relative to the noise a large array of seismographs is needed. It is normal oil-field practice to employ groups of between ten and a hundred seismometers to minimize the unwanted movement, and this technique was adopted by the British Atomic Energy Authority. Modern bomb-detection arrays have instruments spread over several miles, and by recording the output from each detector on magnetic tape it is possible to make the whole array directional, and also sensitive to waves arriving with a selected velocity. Thus by analysing the record of a bomb or earthquake after the event, a great improvement in the ratio of signal to noise can be achieved, and also a distinction between man-made and natural shocks can be noted.

An atomic bomb equivalent in explosive force to one thousand tons of TNT, if exploded in hard rock gives about the same sized shock as a 'magnitude-4' earthquake, of which there are about 12,000 a year all over the world. In what

A typical seismic array. The setting up of two intersecting lines of seismometers, not only facilitates calculation of the speed and direction of seismic wave fronts, but also enables significant traces to be clearly distinguished from local 'noise', such as traffic vibrations. While an explosion (A) opposite, originating in a small space, produces a uniform outward shock in all directions, an earthquake (B), usually originating in a lengthy fault line along which two great rock masses readjust their positions, produces two varieties of shock wave. Thus the bomb trace (A1) shows a single shock which rapidly dies away, while the quake trace (B1) is more complex and sustained

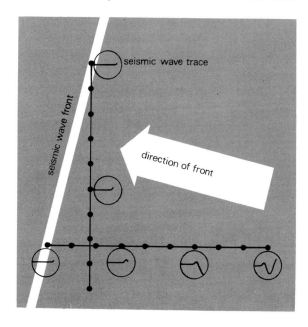

way does the bomb differ from an earthquake? Earthquakes, as we have seen, occur at all depths down to 400 miles, while the deepest hole drilled in the earth goes down only 5 miles, so that any waves which can be shown to come from a deep source must be earthquakes. Many more shocks can be ruled out as bombs by working out the location of the disturbance, since clandestine nuclear tests are generally held on a country's own territory. They might be carried out under the oceans but this is unlikely if a careful analysis of functioning is required. The character of the signal observed is the third criterion that may be used to distinguish bomb from earthquake, and during the past few years methods of accentuating the differences between the two types of source have been improved so that about 95 per cent of earthquake shocks can be identified beyond doubt.

An underground explosion sends out a simple shock wave whose initial movement is an outward push when viewed from any direction. An earthquake, on the other hand, is caused by the splitting or tearing of rock, and generally causes a first shock of more extended duration than does the explosion. Since the source of waves is long instead of being spherical, the earthquake emits waves whose first movement is an outward push for waves travelling in some directions, but is a movement towards the earthquake for waves travelling in a direction at right angles. If we could surround each earthquake by a series of observing stations at a distance of a few hundred miles we could note the directions of the first ground movements; for explosions all would be outwards from the source, while for earthquakes some would be outwards and some towards the source. A network of stations every few hundred miles could probably distinguish bombs from

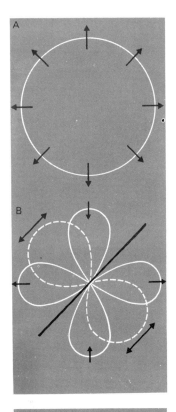

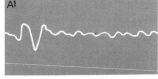

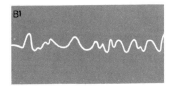

earthquakes but would be very costly, and inspection would still be necessary in doubtful cases.

The modern system of detection works in a much larger distance range of over 2,000 miles. At these long ranges the seismic waves travel steeply down through the core and upper mantle, and have the greater part of their path in the deep mantle, where it appears that there are no irregularities to add complexity to the waves by reflections from different rock layers, as happens in the crust and in the low velocity layer of the upper mantle. The recording arrays are placed at carefully chosen sites where hard igneous rock reaches the surface and gives a uniform connection with the inside of the earth. The records received are therefore a fairly true picture of the signal sent out by the source, with a minimal distortion due to reflections and refractions occurring along the travel path. Most earthquakes, because of the rock movement, produce shear S waves as well as the normal compressional P waves. The two trains of waves can be clearly distinguished at long-distance recording stations, because P waves travel much faster than S. However, some of the S waves are converted to P waves due to reflection and refraction at rock boundaries close to the source; so that for earthquakes the P wave arrival is augmented by some 'pseudo P' waves derived from S. The P waves from an explosion have no such additions, and therefore the P record of a bomb is much simpler in character than that from an earthquake.

It is estimated that about ten of these long distance recording stations would be sufficient to monitor the world, although to give accurate location a network of between twenty and thirty stations would be preferable. Some deep earthquakes show a simple P-wave character, probably because they occur in a uniformly thick rock

A concrete seismometer pit about 7 feet deep. Here earthquake vibrations are detected and amplified before being transmitted electrically to a central seismograph

layer, but these can be distinguished from bombs by their depth. All but 10 per cent of earthquakes can be distinguished by the several large detection arrays now in operation.

The new-look earthquake- and bomb-recording stations will provide further results associated with the variations in the upper mantle, in particular with the low-velocity layer and the possible association of soft, nearly-molten rock with convection currents in the earth. The long-distance earthquake waves, which can be more clearly recorded than ever before, (and with greater accuracy, because the corrections for local rock velocity variations at individual stations are well known) will further knowledge of the liquid core, and of its probably solid inner component.

Nature's arsenal

Future advances in earthquake knowledge may make it possible to predict the larger and more dangerous earth movements. Earthquakes are confined to narrow belts of activity and, while the

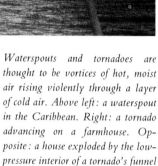

Waterspouts and tornadoes are thought to be vortices of hot, moist air rising violently through a layer of cold air. Above left: a waterspout in the Caribbean. Right: a tornado advancing on a farmhouse. Opposite: a house exploded by the low-pressure interior of a tornado's funnel

reasons for this are beginning to be understood, the mechanisms of earth cracking and the means whereby incipient releases of built-up strain can be recognized are still beyond our reach. There may, of course, be a more sinister aspect to future earthquake study. A complete comprehension of the processes involved may make possible the control of underground rock movements. Just as a wound clock spring stores energy, so the strains that build up over thousands of years inside the earth contain a vast potential for destruction. It is not inconceivable that methods of triggering some of these stores of energy will be devised in the future. Perhaps, for example, a series of appropriately sited off-shore explosions near the California coast would trigger the San Andreas Fault, which has been active for millions of years, and so cause another San Francisco earthquake.

Then again the sun pours energy on to the earth at a rate equivalent to the detonation of 700-million megaton bombs a day. Natural forces

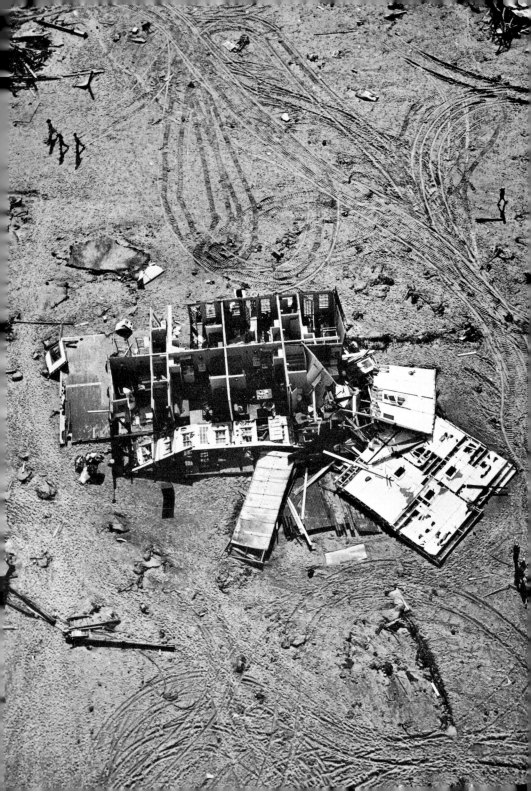

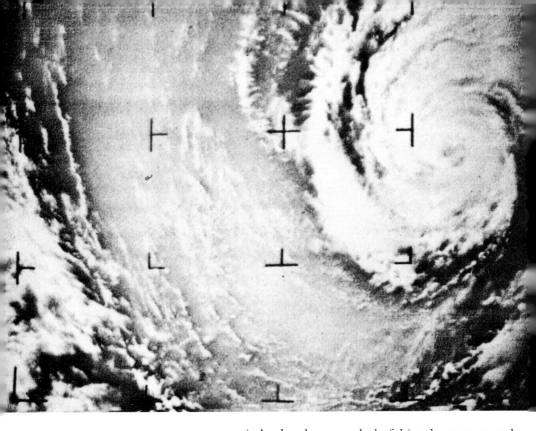

quietly absorb a great deal of this solar energy, and the sea and the atmosphere combine to produce climates that can support human life. Sometimes little packets of energy protrude untidily from the general balance; a tornado, for example, contains easily as much energy as 50,000 tons of explosive, while a thunderstorm may easily be ten times as powerful. Hurricanes work up enough power in their ingenious heat engine to match a thousand-megaton bomb. The Krakatoa volcanic explosion of 1883 – a mere fifty megatons – was small compared with this.

Now that nuclear energy has allowed man to enter nature's league by making explosions of the megaton class, the thought of controlling some natural processes must be occurring to many people. It may eventually be possible to resort to

Opposite: the great cloud spiral of Hurricane Ethel (1964), photographed by weather satellite as it approaches the Florida coast. Left: hurricane damage at Buzzard's Bay, Massachusetts

'geo-warfare', either by setting off catastrophic natural devices such as earthquakes, or by long-term attrition through altering whole climates.

One disastrous effect of the Krakatoa volcanic burst, which can now be simulated by the owners of large nuclear weapons, was the tidal wave, or tsunami, which swept ashore to inundate coastal villages of Java and Sumatra and drown the inhabitants. A series of underwater explosions could be planned to produce even more formidable waves aimed at densely populated centres. Some thought was given to the tsunami as a possible means of clearing enemy-occupied beaches during the Second World War, but the quantity of explosives needed was in those days prohibitive. A less costly alternative might be to use explosives to dislodge clay and mud poised at the top of the continental shelves; the slumping of large volumes of material would again set up a destructive series of waves in the sea.

The explosive type of volcanic eruption, such as occurred in the Aleutian Islands, might sometimes be taken for a nuclear explosion, and could conceivably cause some nervous politician to initiate an exchange of nuclear missiles. Fortunately, however, the zones of volcanic activity are well known, and a mistake of this sort is unlikely. A more randomly distributed type of natural explosion, which might cause confusion, is the impact of a large meteorite. It is believed that the large fast meteorites dissipate so much energy when they hit the earth, that they are 'vaporized' and the effect is similar to that of an explosion. This view agrees, for example, with the evidence of the Arizona crater, which is nearly a mile in diameter. An exhaustive search for a valuable iron deposit formed from the meteorite has only disclosed a fine rain of iron particles spread over the surrounding desert. The chances of a meteorite falling on to a large city are very small, but one could imagine that there would be a great danger of retaliatory action if such a thing occurred. It may be feasible one day to steer meteorites towards the earth by diverting them from their path with the aid of bomb blasts, and it might be possible to direct them to specific targets, although it would be difficult to escape observation.

If large meteorite impacts caused a reversal of the earth's magnetic field, a meteorite 'attack' might have the accidental effect of increasing the cosmic-ray bombardment of the earth by the sun. Ultra-violet rays from the sun would kill life on the earth if their full force was not tempered by absorption in the atmosphere by a layer of ozone. Some ingenious process could no doubt be de-

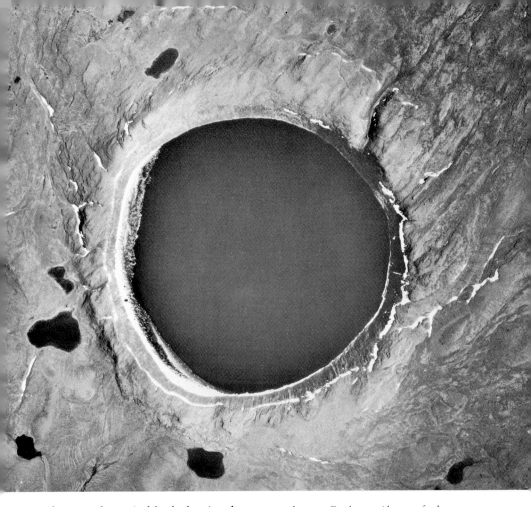

vised to make suitable holes in the protective layer of ozone, thereby allowing an overdose of ultra-violet to afflict an enemy. A more subtle type of change in the atmosphere could affect human life, and may possibly have started. A great deal more coal and oil is burnt now than ever before, and the carbon-dioxide that is being produced may be increasing the proportion of this gas in the atmosphere. Carbon-dioxide helps to keep the earth's surface warm, since it is transparent to the sun's rays but holds in the low-temperature warmth of the earth. If there was a large increase of carbon-dioxide, the earth might

Further evidence of the energy released on impact by a large meteor: the New Quebec Crater, now formed into a lake

warm up a few degrees and life in tropical parts become intolerable. Although it is pleasant to envisage warming the northern fringes of Europe and America, such a process could have serious consequences. If the polar ice caps were to melt, the level of the seas would rise by about 300 feet, and many of the major cities of the world would be submerged.

The control of climate

We do know that the polar ice-caps have played a large part in the earth's climate during the last half-million years. Four ice-ages, during which the Arctic ice spread half-way down the North American continent, and over part of Europe, have left behind them incontrovertible evidence that large-scale climatic changes can occur. It has been suggested that these major cycles of climate are the result of long-term variations in the radiant-energy output of the sun. If this is so, and if mankind wishes to control its environment, further study of the production of the sun's energy emissions and of their interaction with the atmosphere and the earth's magnetic field are essential. The advent of space vehicles most opportunely provides the means for such investigations.

One interesting explanation of recurrent ice-ages is concerned with a property of ice itself. Pressure causes ice to melt, and beneath the weight of thousands of feet of ice in Antarctica and Greenland melting occurs. The water and ice mixture at the base of a thick ice-sheet would allow the ice to slide much more rapidly than it normally flows down a glacier. If this happened in the Antarctic the 800-foot-thick ice-shelves which stretch out 600 miles from land would become greatly enlarged. A general cooling would

result, since more of the sun's heat would be reflected back into space, and the earth would enter a new ice-age. Eventually, however, the colder conditions would cause a freezing of the water beneath the Antarctic ice, and the ice-shelf, no longer rapidly augmented by material from the ice-caps, would break up. The sun's warmth would then fall on a greater area of sea – which absorbs heat instead of reflecting it as ice does – and the earth would warm up again.

If this is the true sequence of events, there would seem to be scope for human intervention: perhaps a nuclear explosion at the base of the Antarctic ice would hasten a new ice-age. This would be to the advantage of equatorial countries, since their climate would be ameliorated while that of their northern and southern neighbours would become unbearably cold.

During the ice-ages the sea-level falls by a few

The desolate peaks of western Greenland protruding through the Arctic ice-cap, which, during past ice-ages, has extended as far south as the northern United States

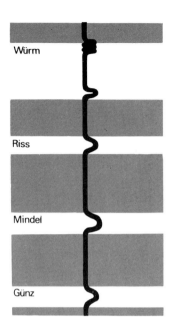

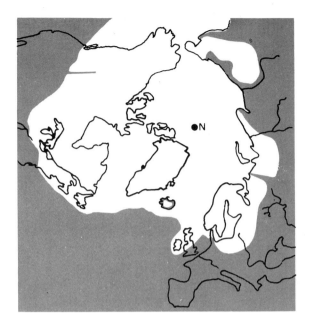

Above right: diagram showing the frontiers reached by the Arctic ice-cap during the four great ice-ages of the past half-million years tabled above

hundred feet because so much water is retained as ice resting on the land. Such changes of sea-level have been deduced from examination of rock layers that have been eroded by wave action, and the history of the recent ice-ages has allowed the changing state of the land to be followed. The geological evidence indicates that these cycles of ice-ages and warm intervening periods are a comparatively new feature on the earth, although they first occurred hundreds of millions of years ago.

It is possible that ice-age mechanisms depend upon the configuration of the land surfaces of the earth, and that continental drift has been needed to get Antarctica and Greenland in suitable locations before a series of ice-ages can occur.

It has been suggested by the Russians that the Bering Straits, that fifty-mile-wide shallow-sea bridge between Alaska and Siberia, should be blocked in order to stop the warm Pacific waters flowing into the Arctic regions. Calculations show that a suitable dam, equipped with batteries of pumps, could withdraw cold water from the Arctic Ocean, and eventually reverse the cold currents that flow into the Atlantic along the Labrador Coast. The Gulf Stream might then run into the Arctic Basin and in so doing would melt the polar ice and form permanent navigational channels across the North Pole. While this scheme would benefit some of the earth's inhabitants it would probably precipitate a warming period of geological history which might have ill consequences for low-lying cities, especially if the Greenland ice-cap were to melt.

One of the more ingenious schemes to upset the world is that of sprinkling carbon black, or ash on the white polar wastes. The new black surface would absorb the sun's rays and would provide the earth with extra heat, and this would lead to the inevitable cycle of increased moisture in the air, a regime of frequent snowfalls and, in the end, a new ice-age. It would probably suit the human race best to put a brake on these natural cycles, and perpetuate a comparatively steady set of climatic conditions.

There are more subtle and less devious ways of affecting the earth's climate than by damming some of the narrow straits of the world and thereby making the climate of what are now the temperate regions too cold, or alternatively, the tropical regions too hot. Experiments over the past few decades have shown that clouds may be made to give up their rain by 'seeding' them with suitable chemical dusts such as silver iodide. An unfriendly nation could, with improved techniques, surreptitiously steal the rain from an unsuspecting neighbour by a planned rain-making operation. The climate in the enemy territory would become dryer–perhaps a welcome change at first—then crops would fail, and eventually, without a harsh word or angry exchange of shots, the victimized nation might be weakened into submission.

Rain-making techniques have been considered as possible means of dispersing the energy of hurricanes, since if the uprising mass of water vapour, which is the working fluid of the hurricane's giant heat-engine, can be condensed to fall as rain the whirling system might be made to dwindle to nothing. No one has yet successfully carried out this experiment, although the United States Navy has recently made several daring attempts to do so. The danger is that the hurricane-depressing technique might simply cause the storm-centre to change course and veer over valuable property, and that compensation claims would be prohibitive. However, once a method of affecting hurricanes by some triggering mechanism has been proved, there could flow wicked thoughts of augmenting the phenomenon and steering it on to selected targets.

Blocking of the Bering Straits could allow the Gulf Stream to flow into the Arctic Ocean. A southward deviation of this great ocean current might be achieved if some obstruction were placed in the 50-mile-wide Straits of Bimini, where the North Atlantic water circulation is funnelled to form the jet-like river of the Gulf Stream. Knowledge of the current flow of the oceans of the world is being collected slowly and laboriously, yet it is of prime importance to understand such phenomena, since quite small man-made obstructions could upset the delicate balance at present reached by nature. So many processes in the world appear to be concerned with vast amounts of energy that can be controlled by small trigger-like mechanisms, that there

is a constant danger of unintentionally initiating a train of events which could spoil the world for man. For the first time in history, man has concentrated in his hands power equal to that of the smaller of nature's manifestations; great dangers lurk among the untold benefits that this power can bestow. Short-term policies of intervention in the natural processes of the earth may have undreamed of long-term consequences. Until man understands fully how the earth has evolved to its present state, and how its comparative equilibrium is maintained, the utmost caution is essential.

The entire cloud cover of the earth's southern hemisphere, on 29 October 1968, is visible in this 'mosaic' of photographs taken by a weather satellite in polar orbit and assembled by a computer. Most conspicuous are the effects of the earth's rotation on the wind systems

GLOSSARY

atoll: a ring of small islands surrounding the lagoon marking the position of an ancient sea-mount

asteroid: a small heavenly body probably formed at the same time as the planets

aurora: beautiful displays of light in the polar skies caused by electrical disturbances in the upper atmosphere

basin: a large depression in the earth's surface which has become filled with sedimentary rocks

batholith: a large intrusion of igneous rock, common in mountain ranges

Carboniferous: the geological period ranging from about 350- to 270-million years ago, when such rocks as coal were being laid down

continental drift (or wandering): movement of the land masses over the surface of the earth

continental rise: an apron of more gentle slope which often exists at the foot of the continental slope and consists of a fan of sediment brought down from the shelf

continental shelf: the shallow-water border of the continent which is geologically integral with the continent

continental slope: the junction between the continental shelf and the deep-ocean floor. At a depth of about 600 feet steepness increases so that in a distance of about 50 miles the 3-mile depth of the deep-ocean is reached

convection: circulation of a fluid due to heating. As applied to the earth, convection currents could account for movements at the surface

core, of the earth: the inner 2,000 miles of the earth which is liquid and probably consists of molten iron under pressure

Cretaceous: the geological period dating from about 130- to 70-million years ago, marked by deposition of large thicknesses of chalk

crust, of the earth: the thin outer section of the earth which contains the rocks familiar at the surface and which is about 3 miles thick under the oceans and about 20 miles thick under the continents

deep trench: valleys in the deep-ocean floor which reach down to about twice the normal depth of the ocean (i.e. up to 6 miles)

gravity: measurement of the local attractions of the earth which helps to elucidate structure in the crust

guyot: a flat-top sea-mount formed by truncation of a volcanic island by the action of waves

igneous rocks: rocks formed by solidification from molten material

layer 2: a hard layer, whose existence is known only from seismic measurements, beneath the soft, deep-ocean sediments, and which may consist of limestone, volcanic lava or shale

low-velocity layer: a sub-division of the upper mantle in which the paths of earthquake waves suggest a softening of the rock and an abnormally low speed of seismic wave travel

mantle: the solid rock layer that lies beneath the crust and extends half way to the centre of the earth, thus forming the greater part of the earth's volume

metamorphic processes: changes in rocks due to temperature, pressure or movement of dissolving fluids

meteorite: a solid body encountered in space by the planets. Meteorites may have been formed by the break-up of planetary bodies similar to the earth

micro-continent: small islands or submerged fragments of continental-type rock which appear surrounded by typical deep-ocean crust

mid-ocean ridge: folds in the crustal rocks of the sea bed which form features of mountain-range proportions down the centre of many of the oceans

Mohorovičić discontinuity: the boundary between the crust and the mantle. At the present time this boundary is only known from earthquake-wave evidence

ocean-floor: the main area of the deep oceans, where the water is 3 miles deep and which covers the greater part of the oceans

P-waves: compressional waves which can travel in both liquids and solids

palaeomagnetism: the study of the fossilized magnetic fields of old rocks

Permian: the geological formation laid down about 270- to 220-million years ago

radioactive heat: heat produced in the mantle or crust by the decay of radioactive elements

rift valley: a large-scale split in the earth's crust causing a well marked topographical feature such as the Red Sea or the east African rift valley

S-waves: transverse waves, which will only travel in rigid bodies

sea-mount: small topographical feature sticking out of an otherwise flat ocean floor

sedimentary rocks: rocks formed of debris deposited in water

seismograph: an instrument for detecting earthquake waves

surface waves: waves which travel in the surface layers of the earth

tektite: small polished glass-like fragments, probably caused by meteorite impact

tsunamis: incorrectly popularly known as tidal waves. Long-period waves travelling at 450 miles an hour, caused by earthquake movements of the crust

turbidity current: a swift-moving stream of mud-laden water which alters the topography of the continental slopes and ocean floor

SELECT BIBLIOGRAPHY

General

Lovell, B. and Margerison, T. (eds.), *The Explosion of Science – The Physical Universe*, London, 1967

Runcorn, S. K. (ed.), *Dictionary of Geophysics*, London, 1967. For detailed references

Spilhaus, A., *Satellite of the Sun*, New York, 1959. Excellent short review of the earth in its cosmic setting

1 The Earth's Origin

Berlage, H. P., *The Origin of the Solar System*, Oxford, 1968

Gaskell, T. F. (ed.), *The Earth's Mantle*, London, 1967

Hoyle, F., *Frontiers of Astronomy*, London, 1958

Jeans, J. H., *Astronomy and Cosmogony*, Cambridge, 1929

Jeffreys, H., *The Earth*, 4th edn., Cambridge, 1959

Lyttleton, R. A., *Mysteries of the Solar System*, Oxford, 1968

Urey, H. C., *The Planets*, Yale, 1952

2 The Drifting Continents

Garland, G. D. (ed.), *Continental Drift*, Ottawa, 1966

Gaskell, T. F., *Under the Deep Oceans*, London, 1960

Hobbs, W. H., *Earth Evolution and Its Facial Expression*, New York, 1921

Runcorn, S. K., *Continental Drift*, New York and London, 1962

du Toit, A. L., *Geology of South Africa*, 3rd edn., New York, 1953

3 The Plastic Mantle

Bullen, K. E., *An Introduction to the Theory of Seismology*, 3rd edn., Cambridge, 1963

Gutenberg, B., *Physics of the Earth's Interior*, New York, 1959

Vening Meinesz, F. A., *The Earth's Crust and Mantle*, Amsterdam, 1964

4 The Core and the Earth's Magnetism

Bullard, E. C., 'The Secular Change in the Earth's Magnetic Field', *Mon. Not. Royal Astronomical Society, Geophysical Supplement* 5, 2 48 (1948)

Jacobs, J. A., *The Earth's Core and Geomagnetism*, New York, 1963

5 The Ocean-Floor

Daly, R. A., *The Floor of the Ocean*, North Carolina, 1942

Hill, M. N. (ed.), *The Sea*, vol. 3, New York and London, 1962

Keen, M. J., *An Introduction to Marine Geology*, Oxford, 1968

Kuenen, P. H., *Marine Geology*, New York and London, 1950

6 Earthquakes and Volcanoes

Gutenberg, B. and Richter, C. F., *The Seismicity of the Earth and Associated Phenomena*, Princeton 1949

Hodgson, J. H., *Earthquakes and Earth Structure*, Englewood Cliffs, N. J., 1965

Runcorn, S. K., *International Dictionary of Physics* Vol. 1., Oxford 1967

Wilcoxson, K., *Volcanoes*, London 1967

7 Mountain Building

Hills, E. S., *Elements of Structural Geology*, London 1963

Runcorn, S. K. (ed.), *Geochronology, Radioactive and Stratigraphic–International Dictionary of Geophysics*, Oxford 1967

Scheidegger, A. E., *Principles of Geodynamics*, Berlin 1958

Jaeger, J. C. and Cook, N. G. W., *Fundamentals of Rock Mechanics*, London 1969

8 Uses and Abuses of Geophysics

Thirlaway, H. S. (ed.), *Experimental Methods in Seismology*, London 1970 (in publ.)

Burtill, J. W. and Whiteway, F. E., 'Application of Spaced Arrays to Analysis of Seismic Body Waves', *Phil. Trans. Royal Society* A 258, p 421

LIST AND SOURCES OF ILLUSTRATIONS

212

The diagrams were drawn by Michael Ricketts

INDEX   *Numbers in italics refer to illustrations*